COIL          
CONSTR

G000124213

by
**B. B. BABANI**

**BERNARD BABANI (publishing) LTD**
**THE GRAMPIANS**
**SHEPHERDS BUSH ROAD**
**LONDON W6 7NF**
**ENGLAND**

## PLEASE NOTE

Although every care has been taken with the production of this book to ensure that any projects, designs, modifications and/or programs etc. contained herein, operate in a correct and safe manner and also that any components specified are normally available in Great Britain, the Publishers do not accept responsibility in any way for the failure, including fault in design, of any project, design, modification or program to work correctly or to cause damage to any other equipment that it may be connected to or used in conjunction with, or in respect of any other damage or injury that may be so caused, nor do the Publishers accept responsibility in any way for the failure to obtain specified components.

Notice is also given that if equipment that is still under warranty is modified in any way or used or connected with home-built equipment then that warranty may be void.

© 1960 BERNARD BABANI (publishing) LTD

ISBN 0 85934 050 3

First Published – July 1960
Reprinted – January 1962
Reprinted – October 1963
Reprinted – July 1965
Reprinted – August 1968
Reprinted – August 1971
Reprinted – August 1972
Revised – August 1974
Reprinted – February 1978
Reprinted – January 1984
Reprinted – September 1985
Reprinted – July 1987
Reprinted – April 1989
Reprinted – July 1991
Reprinted – February 1995
Reprinted – March 1999

Printed and bound in Great Britain by Cox and Wyman Ltd, Reading

# CONTENTS

Page

Chapter 1
Radio Frequency Coil Types and Characteristics . . . . . . . . . 1

Chapter 2
The Design and Construction of Radio Frequency Coils . . . 11

Chapter 3
The Design and Construction of H.F. Chokes . . . . . . . . . 30

Chapter 4
The Design and Construction of Power Transformers . . . . . 32

Chapter 5
The Design and Construction of Low Frequency Chokes . . 44

Chapter 6
Chokes Carrying Direct Current . . . . . . . . . . . . . . . . . . . . 48

Chapter 7
Inter-valve Transformers Carrying Direct Current . . . . . . . 58

Chapter 8
Output Transformer for Single Valve . . . . . . . . . . . . . . . 63

Chapter 9
Air Gap Determination . . . . . . . . . . . . . . . . . . 67

Chapter 10
Push-pull Output and Loudspeaker Transformers . . . . . . . 70

Chapter 11
Input and Inter-valve Transformers (parallel fed) . . . . . . 77

Chapter 13
Construction Details . . . . . . . . . . . . . . . . . . . . . 84

Chapter 14
Methods of Testing . . . . . . . . . . . . . . . . . . . . . . . . . . . 90

Chapter 15
Calculation of Wire Gauge . . . . . . . . . . . . . . . . . . . . . . 94

Chapter 16
Tables . . . . . . . . . . . . . . . . . . . . . . . . . . . . . . . . . . . . 98
    Copper Wire Comparison Tables . . . . . . . . . . . . . . . . 99
    Metric Copper Wire Tables . . . . . . . . . . . . . . . 102
    U.S.A. Copper Wire Tables . . . . . . . . . . . . . . . . 103
    S.W.G. Details . . . . . . . . . . . . . . . . . . . . . . . . . 104
    Resistance Wire Details . . . . . . . . . . . . . . . . . . . . . 106

# Chapter 1

# RADIO FREQUENCY COIL TYPES AND CHARACTERISTICS

Whatever the final function of the apparatus there is no radio and almost no electronic device which does not rely to a great extent on coils. In broadcast receiver design the radio frequency coil with its associated condenser forms the heart of the circuit and the whole excellence of the final output depends upon its working whilst such gear as audio amplifiers, cathode ray oscillographs, relay operators, sound heads and photo-electric devices all depend on coils in the shape of transformers for power supply and coupling, smoothing chokes and audio or radio resonant circuits.

Whether the coil is designed for high frequency working and is a simple helix supported in air or whether it is for power transformation at a low audio frequency, consisting of thousands of turns of wire on an iron core, its basic operation is the same.

All coils exhibit the same qualities, the most important being:

## Inductance

The inductance of a coil (coils are often known as inductors) is the measure of its electrical inertia. To generate a current in a wire and thus develop a voltage across the wire's ends it is merely necessary to move the wire through a magnetic field so that it cuts the lines of force, when the current will depend on the rate of cutting and the number of lines cut, this being the well-known principle of the generator. Moreover, moving the wire one way through the field and then reversing its direction of travel will cause the current to reverse its direction of flow — it will commence at zero and grow to a maximum, fall back to zero as the movement slows and stops and on the return of the wire through the field will grow to a maximum again but in the opposite direction of flow.

This current, of course, is A.C. or Alternating Current, whilst current which always maintains one direction of flow is D.C. or Direct Current.

Current may also be generated in the wire, however, by arranging it in a fixed position and allowing the magnetic field to vary around it, the lines of force growing and collapsing and so cutting the wire as before. Obviously any current so obtained must be A.C. and the frequency will depend on the rate at which the magnetic field grows and collapses, or in the same way, on the rate at which the wire in the earlier examples reverses its direction of travel. One complete alternation from zero to maximum in one direction, back to zero and on to maximum in the other direction and finally back to zero is known as one "cycle" (the number of cycles per second being known as the frequency) and corresponds with one complete revolution of the rotor of a simple alternating generator. Thus we can say that such a cycle takes place over 360 degrees, and if it is desired to inspect only a part of a cycle we can measure any part of a whole cycle along the zero line and give it an angular measurement of, say, 90 degrees or one quarter of the cycle, whilst if we desired to compare two alternative voltages of the same frequency where one grew to its maximum one quarter of a cycle after the other we would say that there was a "phase difference" of 90 degrees between them or that they were "90 degrees out of phase".

In Fig. 1 the continuous line shows one cycle of voltage, the time of the cycle being measured along the zero line in degrees while the broken line shows a similar cycle of the same frequency 90 degrees out of phase. Moreover the crest or maximum point of the broken line is after that of the continuous line cycle, so that it "lags" behind the continuous line by 90 degrees or the continuous line cycle is "leading" by 90 degrees.

One cycle per second is today, more usually called a Hertz (Hz). It may be said here that the normal frequency of the A.C. mains in this country is 50 cycles per second or 50 Hz. While

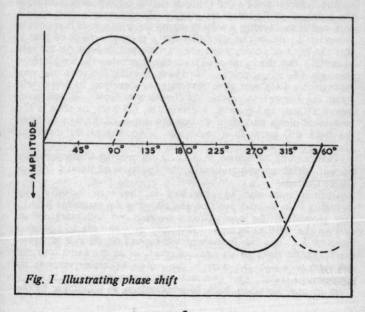

Fig. 1 Illustrating phase shift

2

audio waves extend from roughly 20 to 20,000 Hz and radio waves are arbitrarily divided into bands between roughly 100,000 to 300,000,000 Hz. 1000 Hz are known as a "Kilohertz" (kHz) and 1,000,000 Hz are a Megahertz (MHz).

A coil or inductance, then, may be fed with any of these frequencies depending on the task it is to perform, but to understand what happens suppose a simple coil, a solenoid of a few turns of wire on a simple former, is connected to a battery through a switch. When current flows through a coil it causes a magnetic field to form, the axis of the field being down the centre of the coil, so that if the switch of the above circuit is closed current will flow through the coil and the magnetic field will suddenly grow. As it grows, however, the lines of force, extending outwards, cut the wires of the coil which is the necessary condition for generating a current in those wires. The growing field of a coil always generates this current in opposition to the current from the supply and so it is plain that the full battery voltage will not at first appear across the coil for it will be reduced by the voltage due to the current generated in the coil itself. Obviously this will affect the battery current, making it a smaller flow than it would otherwise be, and not till the whole system is in equilibrium will the current rise to its maximum value. When the circuit is broken the magnetic field collapses and once more the lines of force cut the wires inducing a voltage which this time endeavours to assist the falling voltage and thus endeavours also to bolster up the falling current, these effects, of course, occurring in the fraction of a second. These voltages, generated to oppose any change of condition of the coil, are sometimes known as "back E.M.F.s" and may be quite high, depending on the inductance of the coil. In an electric bell, for instance, it is the self-induced voltage which gives the spark at the contacts and experiment will show that the Back E.M.F. is sufficient to give a smart shock.

This, then, is the effect of the coil's inductance, and obviously it will be of great importance when the coil is fed with A.C. The current is always rising and falling in value so that there will always be a voltage induced by the coil's own field and affecting the current flow in the coil. In a pure inductance the current would lag behind the voltage by 90 degrees, thus in Fig. 1 the continuous line curve could now represent the A.C. voltage across a coil with the broken curve representing the lagging current, so that at full voltage the current is only just beginning to flow.

The unit of inertia, or inductance, is the "henry" as it is proportional to the rate of change of the current. A coil is said to have an inductance of 1 henry when the current, changing at the rate of 1 ampere per second, causes a pressure of 1 volt to be induced across the coil.

The henry is too large a unit for use with radio frequency

3

coils and they are measured in millihenrys (mh.) or in micro-henrys ($\mu$h). The symbol for inductance is L.

## Reactance

A coil has its own ordinary resistance to a steady current, measured as usual in ohms, but as it opposes the sudden changing of currents and voltages it obviously has a secondary effect on A.C. Alternating currents will have to overcome not only the ordinary resistance, but also this "reactance" and the opposition to A.C. of the coil is given by the formula:—

$$X_L = 2\pi fL$$

where $X_L$ is the reactance of the coil in ohms, f is the frequency of the A.C. applied. L is the inductance of the coil in henrys and $\pi$ equals 3.14.

R.F. coils are usually coupled with condensers, and the capacity has an effect on A.C. exactly opposite to that of the inductance. It causes the current to lead the volage, and so the effect of placing inductance and condenser together in a circuit is largely to cancel out their reactances. For a condenser:—

$$X_C = -\frac{1}{2\pi fC}$$

where $X_C$ is the reactance in ohms and C is the capacity in farads. It must be noted that the result is expressed as a negative quantity. Reactances may be added together.

## Impedance

Impedance is denoted by the term Z and when Ohm's Law is applied to A.C. Z takes the place of R, the term for D.C. resistance. When a circuit contains resistance and reactance although both terms are in ohms they cannot simply be added. The formula:—

$$Z = \sqrt{R^2 + X^2} \text{ ohms}$$

must be applied, and where a circuit contains a resistance R ohms, an inductance L henrys and a capacity of C farads in series, the impedance will be:—

$$Z = \sqrt{R^2 + (2\pi fL - \frac{1}{2\pi fC})^2}$$

4

An inductance and capacity together have:—

## Resonance

That is, they respond to a resonant frequency with their lowest impedance if they are in series or with their highest impedance if the inductance and capacity are in parallel. Thus inductance and capacity in parallel and tuned to their resonant frequency develop their highest voltages in phase opposition at that frequency and are the most usual form of tuning circuit as shown in Fig. 2.

The formula for the resonant frequency for either series or parallel circuits is:—

$$f = \frac{1}{2\pi\sqrt{LC}} \times 10^6$$

and it must be noted that here the values have been reduced to working practical values; f is in kilohertz, L is in microhenrys, and C is in picofarads or micro-microfarads (500 picofarads = .0005 microfarads, a common size for tuning capacitors).

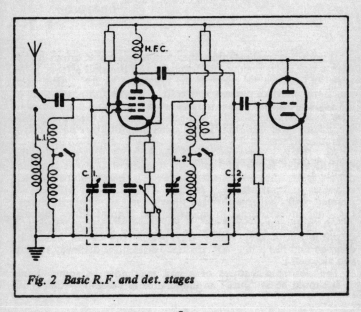

*Fig. 2  Basic R.F. and det. stages*

## Dynamic Resistance ($R_D$)

As a coil and capacity in parallel present a high impedance to their resonant frequency, as is generally desirable so that they may develop a good voltage, the ratio L/C is important and the impedance of such a circuit at resonance may be given as L/CR, this often being known as the Dynamic Resistance. It is plain, therefore, that R, the coil's H.F. resistance, has a large bearing on the dynamic resistance $R_D$ and affects the efficiency of the whole circuit. This efficiency is known as the

## "Q"

of the circuit and may be shown as:—

$$Q = \frac{2\pi fL}{R}$$

where f is in hertz, L is in henrys and R is in ohms. For example, a coil of 100 microhenrys inductance with a resistance at 800 kHz of 8 ohms would have a "Q" of

$$Q = \frac{2 \times 3.14 \times 800,000 \times 100 \times \dfrac{1}{1,000,000}}{8} = 62.8$$

It must be realised that the coil resistance R grows higher with a rise in frequency due to losses and the skin effects of the wire, and cannot be taken as the resistance to D.C. Also a coil can never displace current and voltage by the full phase shift of 90 degrees because a pure inductance is impossible – the turns of wire have resistance and a self-capacity one to the other, while a condenser, on the other hand, sometimes displays quite a large inductive effect.

As "Q" is a measure of efficiency it is also known as the magnification factor of the coil. Clearly if the coil and condenser system has a resonant frequency a charge induced in such a system will not die away rapidly. The condenser will become charged, will discharge through the coil and so reverse its charge, the coil endeavouring to maintain the current flow, will discharge again and so produce a train of waves each of slightly less amplitude until they finally disappear. The circuit is heavily damped and has a low "Q" if these oscillations die away rapidly and vice versa.

The desirable features of a coil may now be summed up. It should be as "pure" an inductance as possible – that is, its

6

self-capacity due to humped turns of wire, heavy former and the design generally must be small, the resistance to high frequencies must be kept low, it must be rigid and of strong construction, for obviously any misplaced or disturbed turns of wire will change the inductance, it must not be susceptible to humidity changes in the atmosphere — dampness might cause leakages from turn to turn — and as the coil has a varying magnetic field it must not be brought too close to any mass of metal for eddy currents would be induced by the field and the efficiency of the coil reduced. For that reason screening cans must be of a correct size which, as shown later, may be calculated.

## Mutual Inductance

The coil has a varying magnetic field in and around it and this will induce a voltage across any other coil in the vicinity if the lines of force are able to cut the wires of the second coil, the wave-form of the induced voltage being a pattern of that on the original coil. This linking of two coils by the magnetic fields around them is known as mutual inductance, and its symbol is M.

Mutual inductance may be either desirable or not, depending on the circuit. For example, in Fig. 2 the second valve, a detector triode, has a reaction coil connected to its anode whose function is to feed back energy into the grid coil. Here mutual inductance is very necessary, but the whole coil set of the detector valve must be screened completely from the coils of the first valve or energy will be fed back into the first stage with consequent uncontrollable instability.

Again, in Fig. 3, the I.F. Transformers have their windings coupled by mutual inductance, but each transformer is carefully screened from all other coils.

The types of R.F. coils used in receivers vary according to the circuits, but Figs. 2 and 3 give some idea of what is needed. Fig. 2 is of a basic circuit for a "straight" receiver, the first being a high frequency amplifier followed by the second stage, a triode detector. Obviously it will be very desirable to make $C_1$ and $C_2$ a ganged two-section condenser but before this can be done the two sets of coils must be similar in all respects so far as the actual tuning windings are concerned. The other windings will put varying loads on these tuning coils in each case, causing damping to some degree but these effects can be balanced in practice. In the first stage the aerial will impose its load on the grid coil via the aerial coil, and in the detector stage the anode coil will be coupled to the grid coil as well as the inter-stage coupling, but if the two grid coils are made identically similar these loads will be balanced by keeping couplings low and, finally, by trimming out stray capacities with the trimming sections of the ganged

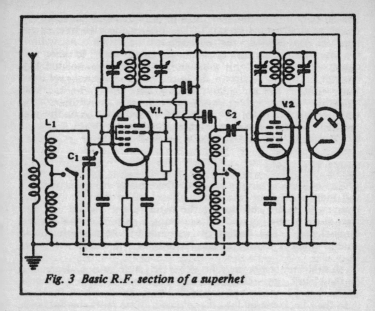

*Fig. 3  Basic R.F. section of a superhet*

condenser.

It will be seen that the grid coil is in two parts in each coil set, one winding being short-circuited by a switch. This winding is the long-wave coil, the unswitched coil in both cases being the medium-wave coil, and these switches must also be ganged. If further wavebands are required their coils may be wound on the same former with extra switching, but for good results on short waves it is advisable to isolate each winding and make it a separate coil with grid and aerial and grid and anode windings as desired. These coils are then mounted round a rotary wafer switch so designed (with an earthing ring) that all coils not in use are short-circuited and earthed to prevent pick-up and other losses, and each set of coils is screened in its own box built round the switch.

For a superhet (Fig. 3) the coils systems are rather more complex. The first stage is a mixing circuit where incoming signals are tuned by $L_1$ and $C_1$ and fed to a triode-hexode. The triode portion of the valve is an oscillator with its own set of coils arranged to tune to a frequency which, no matter what the position of the ganged condenser, is always a constant number of kHz different from the incoming signal. This difference is known as the Intermediate Frequency and the oscillator is usually tuned above, rather than below, the frequency being received.

8

These two frequencies are mixed in the valve and the result is a modulated signal composed of the Intermediate Frequency and the sound signals from the transmitter.

The primary winding in the anode circuit of V1 is tuned by a small condenser to this frequency so that a modulated high frequency voltage is set up across this coil and a similar voltage is induced into the secondary winding also tuned, the two coils together forming an Intermediate Frequency Transformer. The induced voltage is fed to the grid of V2 and again passes through an I.F. Transformer before reaching the detector, V3.

The aerial and oscillator coils are similar to those as used in a straight receiver, but the I.F. Transformers tune to a lower frequency (about 465 kHz) and thus needs more turns of wire and a greater inductance. An I.F. Transformer is, in effect, a Band Pass Filter and as explained in Chapter 2 this greatly assists selectivity in tuning.

There are several methods of improving the selectivity of a receiver. In the straight set reaction can be used in the detector stage to give greater selectivity and volume with a slight drop in tonal quality or several tuned stages may be employed, each consisting of a grid coil and tuning condenser, coupled through an H.F. amplifying valve to the next stage. It is plain, however, that instability would soon be caused by the multiplication of valves,

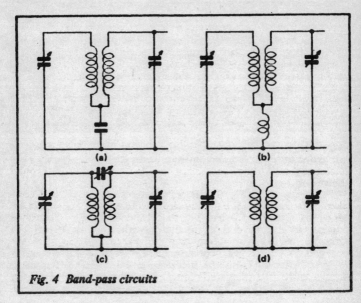

(a)

(b)

(c)

(d)

*Fig. 4 Band-pass circuits*

and generally it is better to reduce the number of stages by using Band Pass Filters instead of single coils. Each Filter requires two tuning condensers instead of one so that a ganged condenser for more than one stage becomes an unwieldy affair, but with a straight receiver good results are obtained by using a Band Pass Filter with the H.F. stage coupled to a single coil in the detector grid circuit.

Band Pass Filters of different types are shown in Fig. 4 and their action may briefly be explained as follows. Where two coils have identical resonant frequencies these frequencies are slightly changed by coupling the coils, one moving higher and one lower. Thus two coils coupled to the correct degree spread a single tuning point over a band although the limits of this band are far more sharply defined than the limits of a tuning point on a single coil. Not only is the selectivity increased, but a station on the band of frequencies has a more even response accorded to its sidebands with a consequent improvement in quality.

## Chapter 2

## THE DESIGN AND CONSTRUCTION OF RADIO FREQUENCY COILS

For home construction, only R.F. coils on open air-cored formers will be considered as apart from S.W. and Television coils, for there is no really satisfactory method for the construction of coils using powdered iron cores.

The steps to be described are:—

1. Design of the coil and determination of inductance.
2. Choice of former and type of wire.
3. Construction.
4. Testing.

### Design

Obviously the whole design of the coil will depend upon the work it is expected to perform. A medium wave tuning coil will consist of a single layer solenoid with or without reaction and aerial coupling coils, multi-range coils will contain both single layer solenoids and bank wound coils for the higher inductances, I.F.T.s will, generally speaking, be bank wound coils made to fit on a dowel former and so on.

For tuning coils it is first necessary to consider the wave range the coil is to cover with due regard to the variable condenser to be used, and here it is advisable to use the formula:—

$$\lambda = 1885\sqrt{LC}$$

where $\lambda$ is the wavelength, L is the inductance in microhenrys and C is the capacity in microfarads. Wavelength has a fixed relationship to frequency, the product of the two being 300,000,000

i.e., $\lambda \times f = 3 \times 10^8$

E. H. Chapman has described one method for evaluating the required inductance from the above formula. Variable condensers have a minimum and a maximum capacity, the stated value being the maximum. The minimum depends on good design and the amount of insulating material used in the construction, and there is a further stray capacity in a tuning circuit due to the wiring of the coil, shields, etc. If, however, the minimum capacity of the condenser is assumed to be zero then the stray capacities of the tuning circuit can be called S, and the formula written:—

11

$$\lambda = 1885\sqrt{L(C + S)}$$

This is the value for maximum capacity; obviously the wavelength for minimum capacity is:—

$$\lambda 1 = 1885\sqrt{LS}$$

Square both equations:—

† $\lambda^2 = 1885^2 L(C + S) = 1885^2 LC + 1885^2 LS.$
* $\lambda 1^2 = 1885^2 LS.$

and by subtracting * from †

$$\lambda^2 - \lambda 1^2 = 1885^2 LC.$$

In this form the formula is very useful for it enables any maximum and minimum wavelength to be referred to the coil and capacity and by transposition L is easily found.

*Example 1*

It is required to tune from 200 to 500 metres using a 0.0003 $\mu$F variable capacitor. Then:—

$$500^2 - 200^2 = 1885^2 \times .0003 \times L.$$
$$\text{and } 210,000 = 1,066L.$$

$$\therefore L = \frac{210,000}{1,066} = 197 \text{ microhenrys.}$$

It should be borne in mind that a tuning system is more efficient so far as range average is concerned the higher the L/C ratio can be made, that is by using a low capacity condenser with a high inductance, but clearly this is limited in the higher waveranges. At low wavelengths the band covered reduces, and adequate coverage is obtained by using several coils with the condenser to cover the bands. As the wavelength falls so will the capacity of the condenser as may be seen by considering a high frequency tuning system with a range of 5 to 8 metres.

*Example 2*

A suitable condenser would be of 0.00005 $\mu$F capacity (generally styled 50 picofarad (pF)).
Then

$$8^2 - 5^2 = 1885^2 \times .00005 \times L.$$
$$\text{or } 39 = 177.7L.$$

12

$\therefore$ L = .22 microhenrys.

The stray capacities in such a circuit would obviously have to be reduced to the smallest degree and the coil would be self-supporting, no former would be used. As the inductance is so low the connecting wires to the condenser must be as short as possible — usually the coil is mounted directly on the condenser terminals — for any loops of wire would add seriously to the inductance, perhaps even doubling its value.

This, then, demonstrates the differences between various types of coils, so far as structural methods are concerned, and a series of general suggestions may be given here.

## Ultra Short Wave Coils. 4 to 10 metres

These may be wound on formers or be self-supporting. If the main desired waveband is about 5 metres self-supporting coils are advisable although if the coil is one of several, as in a superhet, where ganging is necessary a former must be used for the sake of rigidity.

Formers may be of ceramic materials such as are advertised, these formers often being chased with a very shallow spiral so that the wire is more firmly held. It is sometimes stated that copper or silvered copper tubing should be used for Ultra Short Wave work, but this is unnecessary even in small transmitters, let alone receivers. No. 16 or 18 S.W.G. copper wire is perfectly suitable and this may or may not be silvered. The spacing between turns need not be greater than the diameter of the wire used; some spacing is desirable to cut down the self capacity of the coil but greater spacing than one diameter merely has the effect of reducing the inductance disproportionately.

Spaced coils, therefore, are best wound by taking two lengths of the wire to be used and winding them side by side on the former, the spacing wire being stripped away after varnishing (if done) to leave the actual winding spaced out by the wire's diameter. Spacings of smaller size may be made in the same way using various sizes of wire alongside the turns of the coil.

The leads of Ultra Short Wave coils should be made by merely leaving sufficient of the winding wire for connecting up at each end, this being cut down to the smallest length possible when the coil can be tried out in position.

## Short Wave Coils. 10 to 180 metres

These coils may be made on the formers already suggested, on paxolin formers or on ribbed ebonite tubes, the wire sizes being graded down in diameter as the wavelength rises. Above 100 metres spacing will probably be dispensed with, the turns being

13

wound to touch and here insulated wire will be needed. For all general purposes enamelled wire is suitable, the insulation being thin yet strong; the wire must be handled with care, however, for the enamel can be cracked or scratched especially if the wire be allowed to kink. Keep coils of wire wrapped and boxed so that sharp edges cannot rub the insulation.

Once again connections should be made by leaving sufficient of the winding wire at each end of the coil for that purpose.

## Medium Wave Coils. 200 to 600 metres

These coils are usually single layer solenoids wound with the turns side by side and touching. They are made on paxolin formers using enamel, cotton or silk insulated wire, and the ends of the windings should terminate in soldering tags so that connections may easily be made with no risk of poor joints.

## Long Wave Coils. 900 to 2,000 metres (and I.F.T.s)

These coils are most often bank wound, that is they are made of several layers of wire one layer on top of the other. Small paxolin bobbins may be made for the purpose or paxolin cheeks fitted over a cylindrical former, particularly where both Medium and Long wave coils are being wound together. Cardboard or paxolin cheeks might be fitted over ½-inch dowel rod and the turns laid between them the cheeks in this case being removed when the winding has been impregnated with paraffin wax.

Examination of commercially made coils will give ideas and examples.

## The Calculation of Inductance

When the desired inductance has been found by the wavelength formula it is necessary to work out the size of former and number of turns of wire to use to make such an inductance. The writer compared several formulae and tables and found surprisingly wide discrepancies existed between some of them so that finally only two formulae for single layer coils were chosen. Both formulae are adapted from Wheeler's Formula, but whilst the first form uses the total length of the winding, the second uses the number of turns per inch (the winding "pitch"), this being far more convenient for spaced coils.

Wheeler's Formula, adaptation 1:—

$$L = \frac{r^2 \times N^2}{9r + 10l}$$

where L is the inductance in microhenrys, r is the outside radius of the coil in inches and l the length of the winding in inches. N is the number of turns.

*Example 3*

The medium wave coil of Example 1, of 197 microhenrys is to be wound on a paxolin former two inches in diameter and three inches long, so that allowing a ¼-inch overlap at each end l may be taken as 2½ inches. As it refers to the outside radius r should include the wire diameter but only a small error will result if it is made 1 inch for calculation.

Then

$$197 = \frac{1^2 \times N^2}{9 \times 1 + 10 \times 2.5} = \frac{N^2}{34}$$

$$\therefore N^2 = 197 \times 34 = 6698 \text{ and } N = 81 \text{ turns.}$$

This means a pitch of $81/2.5 = 32.4$ turns per inch and from the Wire Tables in Chapter 15 it is seen that S.W.G. 22 Double Silk covered wire wound with turns touching has almost exactly this pitch.

Formula 2 (Wheeler's Formula adapted by Hayman):—

$$N = LX \left[ 1 + \sqrt{1 + \frac{9}{aLX^2}} \right]$$

where N is the number of turns, L is the inductance, a is the outside radius of the coil and X is $20/nd^2$, n being the number of turns per inch and d the diameter of the coil.

*Example 4*

It is required to wind a coil with an inductance of 250 microhenrys on a two-inch diameter former using 20 turns per inch.

Then

$$N = 250X \left[ 1 + \sqrt{1 + \frac{9}{1 \times 250 \times X^2}} \right]$$

and $$X = \frac{20}{20 \times 4} = \frac{20}{80} = .25.$$

So $$N = 250 \times .25 \left[ 1 + \sqrt{1 + \frac{9}{1 \times 250 \times .0625}} \right]$$

$$= 62.5 \left[ 1 + \sqrt{1 + \frac{9}{156.3}} \right]$$

$$= 62.5 \times 2.253$$

$$= 140 \text{ turns}$$

and the winding length will be 140/20 or 7 inches.

An efficient shape for a coil is one where the diameter is two or three times the winding length but this would be bulky and inconvenient for most purposes and the diameter is reduced. Similarly, formulae exist for calculating the optimum gauge of wire to use on a particular coil but this calculation is so intricate that it is omitted. In any case modern valves are so efficient and have such large amplification factors that the efficiency of coils is sometimes reduced to prevent feedback and instability so that the gain in efficiency due to the use of such formulae can be dispensed with.

## Bank Wound Coils

Where coils are to have such high inductances that they are bank wound a formula given by R. E. Blakey in *Radio and Telecommunication Engineers' Design Manual* (Pitman) may be used. For a coil such as is shown in Fig. 5 where a is the mean diameter, b is the winding length and c is the radial depth of the winding all in inches, and N is the number of turns and L is the inductance in microhenrys:—

$$L = \frac{.2a^2 N^2}{3a + 9b + 10c}$$

*Example 5*

A coil of 1,000 microhenrys inductance is to be bank wound on a ½-inch paxolin tube, c and b both measuring ½ inch.

Then a will measure ½ + ¼ + ¼ or 1 inch.

Thus

$$1.000 = \frac{.2 \times b^2 \times N^2}{(3 \times 1) + (9 \times 0.5) + (10 \times 0.5)}$$

$$= \frac{.2N^2}{12.5} = \frac{2N^2}{125}$$

16

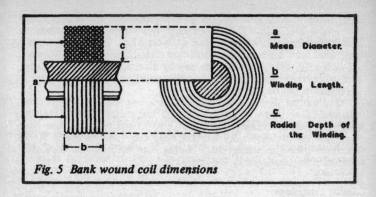

*Fig. 5  Bank wound coil dimensions*

a — Mean Diameter.

b — Winding Length.

c — Radial Depth of the Winding.

So    $1,000 \times 125 = 2N^2$

and   $N^2 = 62,500$ and $N = 250$ turns.

The cross section area of the coil is c x 1 square inches or ¼ square inch so that the wire must be chosen that will wind 250 turns to the ¼ square inch or 1,000 turns per square inch. Reference to the Wire Table shows that S.W.G. 24 D.C.C. is sufficiently close to this value.

When more than one coil is to be wound on a former — for example as in the case of the usual medium and long wave coil — it must be remembered that the two windings are connected in series with all the turns in the same direction of rotation so that when the shorting switch is opened (Fig. 2) the inductances are in series and will be added together. The long wave winding of such a coil, therefore, should have its calculated inductance reduced by the inductance of the medium wave coil so that the sum of the two inductances together equals the required long wave inductance.

### Oscillator Coils

It is the writer's opinion that oscillator coils for superhets are too difficult to design where the tuning arrangements are to be ganged as in the commercial receiver. The complexity of the various calculations may be seen by reference to various designers' handbooks, and even then it is often stated that experimental work on the proposed circuit is necessary to discover the adaptions and changes needed.

The difficulty lies in the tuning arrangements. If the main tuning circuit is to cover, say, from 200 to 500 metres — a range of 1,500 to 600 kHz the oscillator coil for an intermediate frequency of 460 kHz will be working between the points 1,960 to 1,060 kHz. It will be seen that the ratios of maximum to minimum frequencies are different, being 1 to 2.5 for the tuning coil and 1 to 1.84 for the oscillator coil. The steady difference of 460 kHz will not be maintained by straight ganging, therefore, and to correct this a system of padding and tracking condensers is arranged in the oscillator circuit.

In amateur short-wave receivers, it is becoming usual to tune the oscillator quite independently of the aerial or H.F. circuits with a separate variable condenser, and this is probably the best way out of the difficulty for tracking can then be made 100% accurate over the whole dial. Using this method the oscillator coils can be calculated in the ordinary way.

### Aerial Couplings

The signals from the aerial may be fed into the first tuned circuit in a variety of ways which can be reduced to three main methods:—

1. Aperiodic Coil Coupling.
2. Condenser Coupling.
3. Tap Coupling.

Almost all tuning coils are connected with one end earthed and the other feeding the grid of the valve and for convenience these are termed the "earthy" and "H.F." ends respectively.

For aperiodic coil coupling a small aerial coil is wound on the same former which holds the tuning or grid coil, the winding being near the earthy end of the grid coil. The number of turns depends on local conditions but 30 turns in either a single layer or bank wound should be satisfactory for medium and long wave coils, or one quarter of the grid-turns for other coils. The end of the winding nearest the grid coil is earthed, the aerial being taken either to the other end of the aerial coil or to taps which could be included at the tenth and twentieth turns. The aerial coil should be ¼ inch from the H.F. end of the grid coil (Fig. 7e) and both grid and aerial coils are wound *in the same direction*.

Signals will be stronger although some selectivity will be sacrificed by using condenser coupling. In this method the aerial is connected to the H.F. end of the grid coil via a very small condenser — a ceramic trimmer type is suitable — and the capacity is varied for the best results.

Coil and condenser couplings can be combined to give a filter effect, a condenser in series with the earth lead from the coil being arranged to tune the aerial coil to the frequency of any interfering station.

On short and ultra short waves, condenser coupling can be

used but the capacity must be very small indeed to minimise the aerial's damping effect on the circuits with consequent dead spots. Coil coupling is better, a 3 or 5 turn coil being mounted near the H.F. end of the grid coil or between the grid and anode coils of a circuit such as the Franklin self oscillator. Whether the coils are former wound or self supporting the spacing between the grid and aerial coils should be varied to obtain the optimum position.

On these wavebands special aerials are often used together with twin feeders and in these cases the aerial coil is not connected to earth but has one feeder connected to each end.

Tap feeding will cause damping of the coil and will probably put ganged circuits out of alignment. It may be used on a simple circuit, however, and merely consists of various tappings taken from the grid coil to which the aerial may be connected. Alternatively the aerial may be taken to a variable capacitor of up to 300 picofarads capacity, the other terminal of the capacitor being taken to the tap. The nearer the tap is to earthy end of the grid coil the less will be the damping imposed on the circuit and the greater the selectivity. Unfortunately sensitivity falls with increased selectivity. A tap at every tenth turn up to the centre of the coil should give enough adjustment for any aerial.

### Reaction Windings

Where reaction windings are to be used it is difficult to give hard and fast rules. The type of circuit, the valve, the anode voltage and the waveband covered all have their own effects on the oscillatory characteristics of the system. It may be said, however, that for controlled reaction as in Fig. 2 the best form for the coil to take is a small closely coupled winding rather than a large loose coupled coil. This is so in short wave work particularly, where smooth reaction is essential, and in this case the reaction winding is made with wire of a gauge finer than that used for the grid coil, and sometimes even with resistance wire such as Manganin.

Coil sections are shown in Fig. 7 and it will be convenient to consider reaction arrangements for various wavebands.

### Ultra Short Waves

Here the anode coil often becomes a part of the tuned circuit as in the Franklin oscillator or with Colpitt's circuits, and is of the same wire, shape and winding size as the grid coil, being indeed a continuation of the grid coil. Fig. 6a shows a very efficient ultra short wave receiving circuit where grid and anode coils are exactly similar, and regeneration depends on interelectrode capacity coupling inside the valve. Super-regeneration

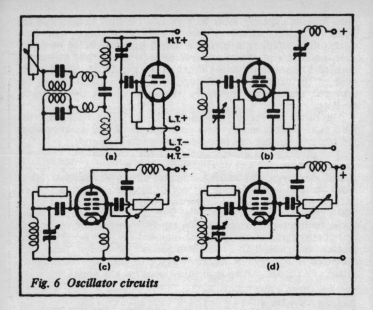

*Fig. 6  Oscillator circuits*

is included and the two larger coils for the feed leads superimpose an oscillation of much lower frequency (20 to 30 kHz) on the ultra high frequency oscillation, thus bringing the circuit to the threshold condition where it is most sensitive and least selective. The net result is a hiss over the whole tuning range which reduces to silence or nearly so when a signal is received. Naturally the system cannot give good quality but for this type of work that is the least consideration. The super regeneration coils are tuned with condensers of about 0.006 $\mu$F capacity so that the inductance for bank wound coils to give the frequencies mentioned above can be calculated.

For an ultra short wave superhet the oscillator section might well be of the Electron-coupled type as shown in Fig. 6d although the circuits of Fig. 2 or Fig. 6b are often used.

Between 10 and 180 metres the range is covered in bands as of 10–25, 18–60, and 50–180 metres or corresponding overlapping bands and reaction is usually applied by the throttle control circuit of Fig. 6b. For mains valves, however, the circuit of Fig. 6c has much to recommend it for reaction is controlled by the potential on the screen of a tetrode and by feedback in the cathode coil which may conveniently be a short wave choke. There is of course no coupling between the grid coil and cathode inductance so that the grid and aerial coils may be simple,

20

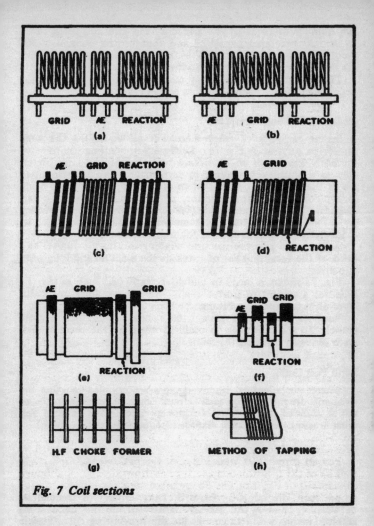

GRID    ÆE    REACTION
(a)

ÆE    GRID    REACTION
(b)

ÆE    GRID    REACTION
(c)

ÆE    GRID
REACTION
(d)

ÆE    GRID    GRID
REACTION
(e)

ÆE  GRID  GRID
REACTION
(f)

H.F  CHOKE  FORMER
(g)

METHOD  OF  TAPPING
(h)

*Fig. 7  Coil sections*

efficient windings on a small former.

Where an anode coil is used it may be arranged either as in Figs. 7c or 7d, being interwound with the grid coil in the latter case. The wires must be insulated but must not touch in any case.

It is suggested that anode reaction coils are given one-third

21

the number of turns of the grid coil, the grid coil being tuned by a 100 picofarad capacitor and the throttle control a 300 picofarad capacitor, although as already mentioned individual circuits may need an adaption to these figures.

Fig. 6d shows the electron coupled circuit where reaction depends on cathode feedback much as in Fig. 6c.

## Medium and Long Wave Coils

In the majority of cases these will be wound on the same former in pairs as in Fig. 7e. The reaction winding has to serve for both wavebands and is wound between the grid coils preferably as a multilayer winding to save space. The best circuit to use is the throttle control system of Fig. 6b, usual values being 500 picofarad tuning capacitor, a 500 picofarad solid or air dielectric reaction condenser, 100—300 picofarad grid capacitor and a grid resistor which with modern practice has reduced its value from 5 megohms to 1 megohm or even less.

As a general rule the reaction winding can have a quarter to a third of the total number of turns on the medium and long wave grid coils.

Fig. 7f shows a medium and long wave coil such as may be used for a midget or portable set. All the windings are multilayer on ½-inch paxolin tubing.

Reaction coils must always be connected in their correct phase. If a circuit fails to oscillate reversing the reaction coil leads generally corrects the fault.

## Band Pass Units

Where two identical tuning circuits are coupled together the resonant frequency of each circuit changes slightly, one to either side of the original frequency, and if the original frequency was f then the new resonant frequencies are:—

$$f_1 = \frac{f}{\sqrt{1-K}} \quad \text{and} \quad f_2 = \frac{f}{\sqrt{1+K}}$$

where K is the coupling factor. Thus a band of frequencies between $f_1$ and $f_2$ is passed, signals within the band being received strongly and those outside the band being cut off more sharply than with other forms of tuning.

A good band-width for normal conditions is 10,000 hertz and for "Bottom Capacity Coupling" the most simple system to arrange is as in Fig. 4a

$$K = \frac{\sqrt{C_1 C_2}}{C_3}$$

and band-width is given by $Bn = fK$.

*Example 6*

Two matched coils are tuned by a $2 \times 0.0005\ \mu F$ capacitor to 600 metres (500,000 Hz) when the sections are fully meshed. The band width at this point is to be 10,000 Hz, therefore as

$$Bn = fK$$
$$10,000 = 500,000\ K$$
and $\quad K = 0.02$

But $\quad K = \dfrac{\sqrt{C_1 . C_2}}{C_3}$

so $\quad 0.02 = \dfrac{\sqrt{0.0005 \times 0.0005}}{C_3}$

$$= \frac{0.0005}{C_3}$$

and $\quad C_3 = \dfrac{0.0005}{0.02} = 0.025$ microfarads.

Supposing, however, that when the value of the capacitors is reduced to $0.0001\ \mu F$ the circuit now tunes to 300 metres (1,000,000 Hz), then

$$10,000 = 1,000,000\ K \text{ or K is now only } 0.01 \text{ and}$$

$$K = \frac{\sqrt{C_1 C_2}}{C_3} \text{ becomes}$$

$$0.01 = \frac{0.0001}{C_3}$$

and $\quad C_3 = 0.01$ microfarad.

The band-width, therefore, will change over the tuning range

23

with consequent varying selectivity. In commercial practice $C_x$ may range from 0.01 to 0.5 $\mu$F.

The coils used for a Band Pass Unit must be similar in all respects so that perfect ganging is obtained, and should be in separate screening cans so that no magnetic coupling is possible between them, when capacity coupling is to be used.

### I.F. Transformers

It will be seen that the I.F. Transformer is no more than a Band Pass Unit so arranged that the Intermediate Frequency is at the centre of the band. In this case, however, the coils are coupled generally by mutual inductance although there is also a capacity coupling due to the capacity between the bank wound coils. R. E. Blakey (*Radio and Telecommunication Engineers' Design Manual*) points out that commercial practice makes the magnetic coupling oppose the capacity coupling by winding both coils in the same direction and connecting either the two starting or two finishing leads to anode and grid of the respective valves.

Particular attention should be paid to making I.F. coils efficient with a high "Q", low loss tuning condensers being used with adequately sized circular screening cans. The main trouble in the construction of I.F. Transformers lies in the adjustment of the coupling between the coils which controls the bandwidth and thus the selectivity, and as these calculations depend on the value of the mutual inductance which is difficult to arrive at it is suggested that experimental methods will give quicker results.

*Example 7*

An I.F. Transformer for 465 kHz is required, both primary and secondary being tuned and identical.

First consider the tuning. The coil will have a self-capacity adding its effect to the capacity of the small tuning condenser so that if 100 picofarad is considered a satisfactory condenser to use the calculations for resonant frequency should be based on almost the maximum value of this condenser, say, 75 picofarad or 0.000075 $\mu$F. Then the capacity of coil and condenser will come well above this in practice, giving room for trimming adjustment either way. The condensers ideally would be of the ceramic mounted air-dielectric rotating type for these are more simple to build in and adjust than the screw operated trimmers, which have an additional drawback in the liability of the screw threads to slip.

The inductance required is discovered from:—

$$f = \frac{1,000,000}{2\pi \sqrt{LC}}$$

24

where f is the frequency in hertz, $\pi$ is 3.14, L is the inductance in microhenrys and C is the capacity in microfarads.

For 465 kHz, then

$$465,000 = \frac{1,000,000}{6.28\sqrt{0.000075L}}$$

and $\sqrt{0.000075L} = \dfrac{1,000,000}{465,000 \times 6.28}$

and $0.000075L = 0.342^2$

or $L = \dfrac{0.342 \times 0.342}{0.000075} = 1,560$ microhenrys.

This inductance may be made as already described in the example of a bank wound inductance, and mounted on ¼-inch paxolin tubing. The transformer will require two such inductances.

## Variable Selectivity

As already explained the band width passed by the I.F. Transformer will depend on the coupling factor — in this case the mutual inductance between the coils — and Fig. 8a shows the coils mounted on a wooden dowel with a push fit so that the coupling between them can be varied till the optimum position is found and then left, an increase in coupling (coils closer together) causing the band width to widen and vice versa.

For constantly variable selectivity, however, either a moving coil or tertiary winding can be employed. Fig. 8b shows one transformer coil arranged to rotate about a central axis about 1 inch from the other, the spindle being pivoted in the wall of the screening or on an internal framework. By using this method it is of course possible to gang a number of transformers by mounting them with the spindles in line and connected together by insulating tubing or rods.

Fig. 8c shows how the coupling and selectivity can be varied by a third coil mounted between the secondary and primary and possessing about one-third of the number of turns on one of the main coils. Control is effected by a variable resistor of 5,000 ohms which is connected across this winding with its moving arm earthed. As the resistance is reduced so coupling is reduced and the selectivity becomes greater.

When using these methods it is advised that one coil of the

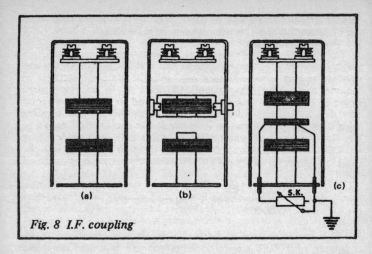

*Fig. 8 I.F. coupling*

transformer is still mounted on a dowel with a push fit. The variable selectivity device is then arranged and clamped to give half of the total effect possible and the transformer response brought to its optimum setting by adjusting the coil on the dowel. The variable device will then give good control on either side of the mean position.

The condensers shown in the figures must be insulated from the screen or any other support, and have any earth leads returned directly to the chassis.

### Coil Construction

When the inductance, method of winding and details of associated coils and condensers have been calculated and decided upon the type of former as already discussed is chosen and the coil wound upon it. Where bank wound coils are to be made it is suggested that a few commercial types should be inspected, they often have the wire laid on spirally in a wave winding which makes a very strong, self supporting coil and reduces the self capacity. This is machine wound, however, and for hand winding it will probably be found sufficiently difficult to keep each layer even, tightly packed without lumping or crossovers and with no break in the insulation. If a coil is to be tapped and is band wound on no account bare the wire and solder the tapping lead so that the joint comes in the centre of the layers. Instead draw out six inches or so of wire, fold the length into a long loop which is taken out through the cheek of the former, if used, and carry the wire back to continue the winding, anchoring the loop in place with the continuing turns. Fig. 7h. The wire can then be bared and connected outside the coil with no risk of a breakdown in the insulation.

Only where wires are completely substantial, as in Ultra Short wave coils should they be used as the coil leads. Thinner wires should be taken to soldering tags and the simplest method of making and fixing these paxolin formers is to drill two small holes at the desired point ¼-inch apart, and to run a double loop of 18 S.W.G. tinned copper wire through them. The winding wire is then soldered to the loop inside the former and carried to the starting point of the winding by the most direct route, being brought to the surface of the former through a third drill hole. This will give adequate anchorage and prevent slipping turns of wire.

When baring the ends of wire for soldering, silk and cotton coverings should be stripped off, not scraped, and enamelled wire should be cleaned by dipping its end into methylated spirit and wiping with a rag. For soldering use cored solder, avoiding killed acid fluxes which will cause corrosion; there should be no chance of a dry or poor soldered joint at any place for bad joints make fault finding doubly difficult.

When the coils are wound it is very desirable to protect them from the effects of humidity and a method which will give them further strength and rigidity is to varnish or wax them. There will be a slight rise in self-capacity but this should not be troublesome.

The best varnish to use is polystyrene. Either immerse the coil in the varnish and allow it to drain very thoroughly or brush the varnish on with a soft brush, working it well into the layers of a bank wound coil. When the varnish is dry spacing turns can be stripped off and bobbin cheeks removed if desired. Coils wound between paxolin washers, as in Fig. 7e, may be left untreated or protected by a layer of cellophane tape.

If the coils are given a protecting layer of wax instead of varnish, it is more simple to be assured of thorough impregnation especially in the case of bank wound coils. Beeswax is melted down and then boiled, to make sure that any water contained in it is expelled, and then the coil is dipped in the molten wax and allowed to remain until all the air bubbles are driven off and cease to rise.

Wooden formers or the dowels suggested for the I.F. Transformers should be boiled in the wax before use, once again remaining until air bubbles cease to rise.

When the wax has set the coil will be very firm but all surplus wax must be drained away.

## Screening

Enclosing a coil in a screening can always result in some drop in efficiency together with a drop in inductance, these losses being very serious if the can is not of an adequate size. It is possible, however, to calculate the inductance drop due to a can so that when the coil is designed this loss can be allowed for by adding it to the correct inductance value of the coil.

A rough rule for keeping the "Q" of the coil high is to make the diameter of the can at least twice that of the coil; greater spacing would be beneficial but would make the apparatus bulky in most cases.

A. G. Bogle (*Journ. I.E.E., Vol. 87*) gives that for a coil mounted coaxially in a can of reasonably thick non-magnetic metal, where coil and can are cylindrical and the gap between the ends of the winding and the ends of the can is equal to or greater than the gap between the sides of the coil and the sides of the can.

$$L_2 = L \left[ 1 - \frac{1/g}{1/g + 1.55} \times \frac{b^2}{a^2} \right]$$

where $L_2$ is the inductance screened, L is the inductance unscreened, l is the length of the coil winding, g is the gap between the side of the coil and the side of the can (equal all round), a is the diameter of the can and b is the diameter of the coil, all measurements in inches, and the formula to hold for frequencies of or over 100 kHz.

*Example 8*

The coil of examples 1 and 3 is to be screened. L = 197 microhenrys, l = 2.5", b = 2" and if the can is 4" in diameter g = 1" and a = 4".

Then

$$L_2 = 197 \left[ 1 - \frac{\dfrac{2.5}{1}}{\dfrac{2.5}{1} + 1.55} \times \frac{2^2}{4^2} \right]$$

$$= 197 \left[ 1 - \frac{0.625}{4.05} \right]$$

$$= 197 \times 0.846$$

= 166.66 microhenrys, the new inductance.

Thus is the screened inductance is still required to be 197 microhenrys the percentage difference due to the screening effect must be added to the original inductance of the coil.

## Testing Coils

Coils when wound may have several tests applied to them but for home construction it will be sufficient to make a simple continuity check with a battery and lamp or instrument and to measure inductance if a bridge is available or can be made. Where coils are to be matched, however, it is necessary to use a signal generator and valve voltmeter. Although the method is easy, it gives good results. Each coil is connected in turn across a small condenser and the output from the signal generator fed into the tuned circuit thus formed by connecting its leads across the coil. The voltage across the coil is measured by the valve voltmeter and when the signal generator is tuned through the resonant frequency the voltage rises sharply through a peak. Each coil is tested in this way and if the peak voltages occur at different settings of the generator that coil with the highest frequency setting has the lowest inductance and the other coils must be reduced to the same value. This is done by removing from them one turn of wire at a time until the resonant point of each coil falls on the same setting of the signal generator.

Naturally this method of adjustment should not be carried beyond narrow limits and two or three turns should be the maximum number removed. If a greater discrepancy between the coils the low inductance coil should be inspected for faulty winding or shorting turns.

## Chapter 3

# THE DESIGN AND CONSTRUCTION OF
# H.F. CHOKES

In the ordinary receiver the H.F. Choke can never be better than
a compromise — even for one waveband a properly designed
choke can have its maximum efficiency at only one frequency
although the drop in response is gradual enough for working all
over the band and one choke will suffice for the medium and long
wavebands — and the cause of this is easily seen when the theory
of the choke is understood.

The purpose of the H.F. choke is to allow low frequency
signals to pass on to further circuits after separation from their
H.F. carrier whilst blocking the H.F. and by-passing it to earth
(as in the case of the ordinary triode detector); to prevent H.F.
from entering the high tension supply; to pass H.F. from radio
frequency amplifiers to following circuits with as little loss as
possible, as in Fig. 2, together with other less frequently used
applications. A high resistance will oppose a flow of H.F. and is
sometimes used in the anode circuits of radio frequency amplifiers and detectors, but an H.F. choke will perform the same
function without the high voltage drop which must of necessity
appear across such a resistance.

The action of the choke depends upon the fact that if a radio
frequency signal is applied to a long wire whose electrical length
is ¼ of the wavelength of the signal applied a standing voltage
wave is set up on the wire or, in other words, the wire behaves as
if it had very high impedance at one end and very low impedance
at the other. If one end of the wire is earthed (via a condenser)
therefore, the other end of the wire opposes the passage of H.F.
currents of the resonant frequency.

Thus all that is required is to wrap the length of wire into a
more convenient form, and it will be realised that a high number
of turns will be necessary for the lower frequencies. The
characteristics of the choke are not greatly changed by coiling
the wire.

For the medium and long wavebands it is not economical to
construct H.F. chokes but should it be desired to do so a
convenient method is to slot an ebonite rod 1 inch in diameter
with six equally spaced rings each ¼ inch deep and ¼ inch wide,
winding 500 turns of No. 34 S.W.G. enamelled copper wire in
each slot (Fig. 7g). The windings, of course, are carried from slot
to slot and are all in the same direction of rotation. This gives
3,000 turns of wire, the two ends being anchored to soldering
tags or terminals threaded into the ebonite former.

When a set is to receive medium, long and short waves a short
wave choke should be wired into circuit before each medium and

long wave choke — that is nearer the valve in question — the chokes being in series. Short wave chokes are simple to calculate by using the ¼ wavelength ruling; for example a choke for wavelengths around 50 metres would have 12.5 metres (41 feet) of No. 34 S.W.G. enamelled or silk covered wire wound on to a narrow paxolin former in three or four small banks, the banks being spaced to cut down the self-capacity. For Ultra Short Wave work the wire becomes very short and is then best wound on to a glass tube of suitable diameter in a single spaced winding.

Transmitter and oscillator chokes for amateur equipment may be made in the same way with any necessary allowance in the wire gauge to suit the probably heavier currents flowing.

Chokes are better unimpregnated, and if protection is thought to be necessary for the 3,000 turn choke it is best provided by winding cellophane tape round the former or by cementing a sheet of celluloid over the wire.

The only test necessary for the choke is a simple continuity check.

In all circuits the choke should not be allowed to approach other wiring in the same valve circuit, particularly if it is an anode choke as is usually the case. The bypass condenser lead should go directly to earth by the shortest route, and in Ultra Short Wave equipment it is beneficial to run all bypass leads to one main connecting point on the chassis.

Medium and long wave chokes can be screened if desired if the precautions observed in screening coils are noted.

# Chapter 4

## THE DESIGN AND CONSTRUCTION OF
## POWER TRANSFORMERS

Transformers may be regarded either as impedance or voltage matching devices, and when designing power transformers it is more convenient to consider the voltage ratios.

Transformers for power supplies consist of two coils, or sets of coils, wound on an iron core to assist the coupling between them and thus improve their mutual inductance. Power from the A.C. mains is supplied to one coil or set of coils and the magnetic flux set up in the iron core and around the coil induces currents in the second set of coils, the voltages across these coils being either higher (step up) or lower (step down) than the voltage supplied.

The coil to which power is fed is known as the primary, those from which power is taken are known as secondaries, and in radio power transformers are of both step up and step down windings.

The size of each winding bears a very definite relationship to the power supplied to or drawn from it, the number of turns controlling the voltage and the resistance, expressed as the diameter of the wire, controlling the current.

The number of turns varies inversely as the size of the core.

The core is built up of thin sheets of iron in the form known as a laminated core, and this is a method used in practically all A.C. apparatus. Clearly the rapidly varying magnetic flux will induce currents in the core as well as in the windings around it and if the core were one mass of metal with a very low resistance the current so induced would be exceedingly high. It is necessary therefore to increase the electrical resistance of the core which can only be done as described, by splitting it into thin sheets and insulating each sheet from the next. Eddy currents will still flow but the total loss of power so caused will be far less than it would otherwise have been.

Laminations are insulated in several ways — by chemical treatment of the metal surface, by varnish, by very thin cemented paper — and there are two main shapes of laminations, the E and I type and the T and U type, both sets giving a three legged core (Fig. 9a).

When the laminations are being inserted into the finished coils on their former they must be alternated, that is an E must go in from the left with an I from the right then an I from the left and an E from the right and so on, the laminations being brought into tight contact with no air gaps.

The cross sectional area of the core, Fig. 9b, is chosen from the formula given by *The Radio Designers' Handbook*, Iliffe, where

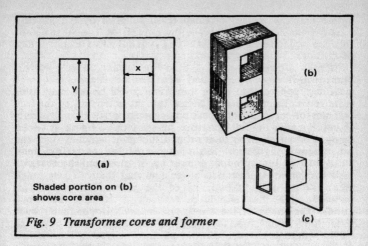

*Fig. 9  Transformer cores and former*

$$A = \frac{\sqrt{W}}{5.58}$$

where W is the volt-amperes output, and A is the cross section area in square inches.

*Example 9*

A transformer is to supply 300 volts 100 mA's, 4 volts 2A and 4 volts 4A.

The total output, therefore, is

$$300 \times \frac{100}{1,000} + 4 \times 2 + 4 \times 4$$

$$= 30 + 8 + 16 = 54.$$

Therefore,

$$A = \frac{\sqrt{54}}{5.58} \quad \text{or} \quad 1.3 \text{ square inches is the necessary core area.}$$

The formula connecting the number of turns in a winding with a given voltage, size of core, frequency and flux density is

$$E = \frac{4.44 \times F \times H \times N \times A}{100,000,000}$$

where E is the voltage supplied to or supplied by the winding, F is the mains frequency, H is the number of lines of magnetic flux per square inch in the iron and A is the cross sectional area of the core.

If E is allowed to equal 1 then the calculation will give the number of turns per volt for any winding on that core.

It is supposed that often transformers will be rewound using materials to hand, and in this case the characteristics of the iron will not be known. The best compromise in such conditions is to let H equal 60,000 lines per square inch, a figure at which many power transformers are run, although if winding space and other conditions permit this may be reduced to 50,000 lines. A, it must be remembered, is built up of laminated sheets which have insulation on one side at least so that the actual magnetic area will be only 90% or so of the geometrical area. This measured area, then, should be reduced by 10% for the calculation. The shape of the core must be well proportioned, each outer limb having half the width of the middle limb on which all the windings are placed in layers, thus occupying the window space "x x y" of Fig. 9a. The general order of the windings is primary inside, nearest the limb, the H.T. secondary and the heater windings outside, of which there are usually at least two, one to supply the rectifier heater and one for the valve heaters of the receiver or apparatus.

The regulation of the transformer is very important — that is the virtue of its having only a small output voltage variation with varying current loads — and depends to a great extent on the iron of the core, the shape of the core and the filling of the window space with windings, there being no large gap between the last layers of wire and the outside limbs. The core must be large enough and the wire diameter fully adequate to handle the loads expected.

The main losses in a transformer are "iron" and "copper" losses; those watts lost due to eddy currents and the purely magnetizing effect on the core, and the watts lost due to the currents flowing in the resistances of the windings. Theoretical transformer design requires these losses to be equal when the transformer will be at its most efficient working level, but for the purposes of small transformer design it will be sufficient to base all calculations on a theoretical efficiency of 80% instead of 90% or so which, with care, will be obtained. These losses will be dissipated as heat and any transformer which heats up in working to anything but a small degree is inefficient and wasteful. Power is being lost, regulation will be poor and insulation will be subjected to the most undesirable strains. A good transformer will work for hours with a temperature rise which can scarcely be observed by touch.

The windings are usually on a former. Fig. 9c, a tube which

will fit the core tightly with end cheeks to clear the window space, and through which the leads pass. Such a former can be made of stiff cardboard well shellaced, or of thin paxolin. Cardboard is quite suitable for ordinary voltages; the tube is first made to fit the core and the end cheeks are fitted, then the whole is well varnished and allowed to set hard. It will perhaps be best to follow the design and construction of a specimen transformer throughout.

*Example 10*

A transformer is to be made with the specification: Primary to be tapped to 210, 230, 250 volts, Secondaries, 350—0—350 volts, 120 mA's, 6.3 volts 3A and 5 volts 2A.

The watts ratings, therefore, are:—

350 x 120 mA's (only half the H.T. winding
supplies current at one time) = 42 watts.
6.3 x 3 =                            18.9 watts.
5 x 2 =                               10    watts.

giving an output total wattage of          70.9 watts.
or, say, 71 watts.

The cross sectional area of the core should be at least

$$A = \frac{\sqrt{71}}{5.58}$$

or 1.5 square inches, and assuming an efficiency of 80%, which should certainly be bettered in practice, the input wattage is therefore

$$71 \times \frac{100}{80} \text{ or } 88.7 \text{ watts.}$$

At a working voltage of 230, therefore, (the usual mains voltage) the primary will take 88.7/230 amps or 0.4 amps, nearly, and the wire must be chosen to carry this current safely. The question of insulation enters here.

Commercial transformers, as inspection will show, are most often wound with enamelled wire, but conditions are different from those pertaining to home construction. The commercial transformer is machine wound so that the wire can be, and generally is slightly spaced between turns so that there is no rubbing of the enamel, whilst the wire tension can be more accurately controlled. For amateur construction enamelled wire can be used but on no account should it be wire taken from old coils or transformers. It must be new and every precaution must be taken to ensure the covering is not cracked, kinked or rubbed for a breakdown in insulation in any winding renders the whole transformer useless.

Probably the best plan is to use enamelled wire with the added protection of a single silk covering for the heavier primary winding.

A suitable core is now chosen, one with an area of 2 square inches (reducing to an electrical area of 1.8 sq. ins.) being before the writer.

The turns per volt formula becomes, then,

$$1 = \frac{4.44 \times 50 \times 60,000 \times N \times 1.8}{100,000,000}$$

but if desired a factor can be produced relating to all transformers where H is taken as 60,000 by leaving out the terms N and A.

This factor, obviously, for 50 Hz mains, is

$$1 = \frac{4.44 \times 50 \times 60,000}{100,000,000} \times AN$$

$$= 0.1332 \, AN$$

so that the formula for this transformer becomes

$$1 = 0.1332 \times 1.8 \times N$$

$$= 0.24N$$

and $N = \dfrac{1}{0.24}$ or 4.2 turns per volt.

The windings can all be calculated, then, the primary having $250 \times 4.2 = 1,050$ turns tapped at 966 and 882 turns, the secondary has $700 \times 4.2 = 2,940$ turns, centre tapped, the valve heater secondary has $6.3 \times 4.2 = 26.5$ turns and the rectifier secondary has $5 \times 4.2 = 21$ turns.

The size of wire, as already shown, affects the current flowing in the winding, and for this type of transformer the gauge may be chosen on the basis of a current flow of 2,000 amps per square inch.

The primary draws 0.4 amps so from the wire table it will be seen that S.W.G. 26 enam. and single silk will be suitable; for the H.F. secondary enamelled wire with an interleaving of thin waxed paper between each layer will be used, and to carry the 129 mA's S.W.G. 34 will be suitable.

S.W.G. 18, enamelled, will suit both heater windings, and to make up losses one extra turn is usually added to the calculated figures for these two coils.

It is now necessary to pay some attention to mechanical details and to check over the dimensions of the former. The size of the window space, "x x y", as shown in Fig. 9a, is $1\frac{1}{8}''$ x $1\frac{5}{8}''$ and the former may be supposed to be made of one-eighth material, card or paxolin. This will reduce the available space in three directions, leaving the depth of the window one inch and the length one and five-eighths inches. The space taken by each winding must now be calculated.

### The Primary

S.W.G. 26 enam. and single silk winds 48 turns to the inch, so that the former will take 48 x $1\frac{5}{8}$ turns per layer, or 78 turns. The number of layers will be 1,050/78 or 14 layers and the height will therefore be $\frac{1}{3}''$.

### The H.T. Secondary

S.W.G. 34 enam. wire winds 100 turns per inch so that each layer will contain 100 x $1\frac{5}{8}$ or 162 turns. The number of layers will be 2,940/162 or 19 layers, and these will be one-fifth inch high.

### Heater Secondaries

S.W.G. 18 enam. wire winds 19.7 turns per inch so that one layer will contain 19.7 x $1\frac{5}{8}$ or 32 turns so that each heater winding will fit into a layer comfortably, and the whole wire height of the two windings together will be under $\frac{1}{8}''$.

The total height of the wire alone, then, is $\frac{1}{3} + \frac{1}{5} + \frac{1}{8}$ or $\frac{2}{3}$ inch, leaving $\frac{1}{3}$ inch space for insulation.

When the former is made, shellaced and perfectly hard the cheeks may be drilled for the leads using the figures above as guides or the holes may be made as the work progresses providing there is no chance whatever of damaging the wire insulating in any way. The primary is wound first, the wire being cleaned properly with spirit, not by scraping, and having a flexible lead soldered to it. The soldered joint must be perfectly smooth with no sharp points or projecting wire ends, and it is then covered with insulating sleeving which carries the flex lead through the cheek. The wire is then wound either by hand or by a simple winder, which is much to be preferred. All that is needed is a spindle turning in end plates or bearings, a handle at one end.

Two adjustable cheeks are then mounted on the spindle to grip the former tightly, the spindle (which might well be a long screw threaded rod) passing through the centre hole of the former. The former is then rotated with the right hand, the wire being fed off its reel and tensioned evenly with the left. The turns should be laid evenly side by side and counted as they are put on, in the absence, as is likely, of a mechanical counter it is convenient to mark every twenty turns on a sheet of paper.

The primary winding is not interleaved so that when the end of one layer is reached the wire is wound straight back on itself and tension must not be over tight for each corner of the former presents a sharp right angle bend to the wire whilst the lower turns have to sustain the considerable strain of all those windings above them.

It is necessary to understand the effect of one short-circuiting turn in any winding. It would consist of a very low resistance loop in which, therefore, a very high current would be induced, this causing heating and consequent burning of the insulation on adjoining turns of wire, whilst the extra load reflected into the primary might cause that winding to be overloaded to the fusing point. It must be realised that the current flowing in the primary depends entirely on the load being drawn from the secondaries, with the secondaries disconnected the only current flowing in the primary is the small core magnetizing current and the winding acts as a choke.

The taps for the various primary voltages can be taken out in the same manner as the taps on coils, by drawing out a loop of wire and returning the wire to the next turn without any breaks or joins, or a flex lead may be soldered to the winding at the correct turn and well insulated. Whenever possible taps should be arranged to fall at the end of a layer so that they may be passed straight through the former cheek. If, however, they have to pass over several turns the insulation must be perfect and on no account must unevenness of winding be allowed in the next layers. Any bump in the centre of the coil will be magnified in the later layers with a corresponding strain on wire and insulation.

When the primary is finished, and a flex lead soldered to the last turn, the winding must be insulated from the following coils. The best material is Empire Cloth interwoven with glass fibres and known under such names as Glassite, but plain Empire Cloth may be used. Every part of the primary must be covered, the insulation being carried up snugly to the former cheeks.

Many transformers have an electrostatic screen wound over the primary to prevent interference from the mains being induced into the secondaries. It consists simply of one layer of fine insulated wire − S.W.G. 34 enam., for example, one end of the wire being anchored internally and the other brought out through insulating sleeving. The end brought out is earthed to the receiver or other apparatus worked from the transformer. Naturally just as much attention must be paid to the insulation of the screen as of any other winding; no load is taken from it as only one end has a connection but shorting turns would give rise to the same heavy overloads mentioned above.

If the screen is included another layer of Empire Cloth is wound over it, giving a smooth, even base for the H.T. winding. Again a flex lead is soldered to the start of the coil and insulated but in this winding a sheet of thin paper is interleaved between each layer of wire. Excellent paper for this purpose can be obtained by stripping down an old paper condenser of the Mansbridge type, any punctured parts of the paper being discarded. On each wire layer one turn of paper is wound, fitting tight up the cheeks, and the wire is wound back over it to form the next layer.

At the centre tap a flex lead is soldered to the wire and anchored firmly in the coil, the flex being taken through the cheek and the joint, as before, being perfectly smooth and insulated. When the H.T. winding is finished another layer of Empire Cloth or Glassite is laid over it and the valve heater winding made, the commencing lead through one cheek and the finishing lead through the other. A layer of Empire Cloth or Glassite separates it from the last winding, that for the rectifier heater which is put on in the same way.

Study of any power pack will show that the full H.T. voltage is established between the H.T. and rectifier heater windings and the insulation between them must be perfect. Any breakdown here will immediately ruin both transformer and rectifier valves.

When the former is wound it is given a last covering of cloth and the laminations are inserted into the centre aperture in order as already explained. The stampings must be inserted carefully for it may be possible to run a sharp edge or corner into and through the former material, cutting or scraping the primary winding.

The laminations must be clamped into a solid mass with wooden or metal clamps which can also be drilled to provide fixing holes for bolting the transformer to its chassis.

## Testing

The first tests to be given the transformer are continuity and insulations checks, these being performed with a neon lamp worked from the A.C. mains. One mains lead is taken to the metal core of the transformer and the other, through the neon lamp, to each lead from the windings in turn. Any lighting of the lamp indicates a short circuit from a winding to the core which must be rectified. The next test is to check the insulation between the windings; transfer the lead from the core to the common primary wire and test the screen and secondary leads in turn with the neon lamp, transferring the mains lead from the primary to each secondary in turn as the test progresses.

Again, any lighting of the lamp indicates a short circuit, but actually any short circuits so discovered would be due to very careless workmanship and are unlikely.

Finally the continuity of each winding is checked with the neon lamp, connecting it across each coil in turn, not forgetting the tappings, when the lamp should light.

If a small megger is available really valuable insulation tests can be made but care must be used to choose a voltage below any break-down voltage calculated for the insulation used. However, as the peak voltage across the H.T. secondary of the transformer described would be almost 1,000 volts the transformer should certainly show a resistance of many megohms at 2,000 volts between windings.

When the transformer has been checked for insulation and continuity, its voltage ratios can be checked. The primary is connected through the suitable tapping to the A.C. mains, with all the secondary leads well separated so that no two can short-circuit together.

Never check secondaries by touching the leads together to produce a spark — results are spectacular but impose an unnatural strain on the primary and should the transformer have been wound to close limits the high currents flowing will probably fuse a winding.

Switch on with the primary only in circuit. After a slight thump or click there should be very little hum from the core, and any appreciable noise indicates loose laminations which must be tightened. Let the primary run alone for ten minutes and check for warming up. Any temperature rise indicates either a totally incorrect winding size or shorting turns in any one of the windings.

In either case connect an A.C. voltmeter across each secondary in turn, and note the voltages obtained from each. If they are all low, and the transformer is heating up, it is likely that there are shorting turns in the primary. If one voltage is low there are probably shorting turns in that secondary alone. Any winding with shorting turns must be rewound but if the work has been done properly and good wire used there is very little reason for this fault to occur.

Check the voltage on the H.T. secondary from the centre tap to either end of the winding — there should be no difference in the readings, or at most one of only one or two volts. The heater winding voltages will be a little high but when the load is applied they will fall to their correct value.

If the voltages are correct the transformer may be finished and coupled up, but a power test is advisable. For this, non-inductive resistors of adequate watts ratings must be used in the following manner.

The H.T. secondary supplies 350 volts at 120 mA's or, disregarding the centre tap, 700 volts at 60 mA's. This is a wattage of 42, the resistance needed being

$$R = \frac{700 \times 1,000}{60} \text{ or } 11,666 \text{ ohms}$$

which might well be made up of lamps whilst the L.T. windings can be tested on load using a resistor of 20 watts rating, 2.1 ohms for the valve heaters winding and one of 10 watts, 2.5 ohms for the rectifier winding, or, of course, the actual valve heaters to be used.

The test should run for an hour at least and the rise of temperature of the transformer tested — in commercial practice it might rise by 40° centigrade, but this should be bettered.

When the testing is completed the transformer can be finished. If the core is clamped satisfactorily and the transformer is to be permanently installed nothing more need be done but if the transformer is to be used for experimental work the leads should not be used for direct connections but should be taken to terminals, mounted on paxolin in the form of a strip secured by two of the clamping bolts.

If the transformer can be mounted in an iron case or can, any stray fields which might give rise to hum can be suppressed. The old case of a choke or transformer could be used or even a heavy tin. In this case the leads should be brought out through insulating bushings or the terminal strip should be well insulated. The case or can should not be allowed to touch the winding at any point, both to assist in insulation and also to allow air to circulate freely for the purposes of ventilation.

In some cases the most tiresome and painstaking work, that of winding the H.T. secondary coil, can be avoided. The transformer can be made on a proportionately smaller core with primary and secondary windings to feed the valve and rectifier heaters, the H.T. being drawn straight from the mains by using the rectifier as a half-wave device (Fig. 10b). This system is used extensively in television design.

The operation of the power pack as a whole may here be considered, with reference to Fig. 10a, where the transformer just described is shown in its circuit. The H.T. secondary has been wound to give a R.M.S. voltage of 350 which means that the peak voltage will be 350 x 1.414 (peak value of a sinusoidal wave).

41

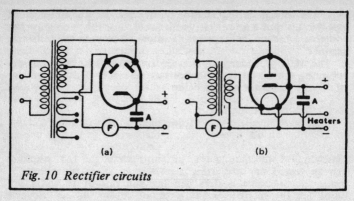

*Fig. 10  Rectifier circuits*

Thus the rectifier anodes will have peak voltages of 495 volts, the whole winding having a peak voltage across it of 990 volts and even after the voltage drop due to the rectifier is allowed for the capacitor. A has a voltage across it well in excess of 350 volts – probably 450 volts. This explains why the voltage rating for this capacitor is necessarily high; a 350 volt working component would soon fail in this position.

The actual value of the condenser in microfarads is more or less of a compromise for the final output voltage of the power pack depends to a great extent on the size of the reservoir. If it were to be omitted the output voltage would be very low and as it rises in capacity so the output voltage rises towards the peak value. Before the peak voltage is reached, however, the condenser is excessively large (and expensive), but moreover, it would be drawing very heavy currents from the rectifier valve on each surge or peak of the cycle and the valve would soon lose its emission.

Valuable protection to the rectifier and transformer can be given by inserting simple fuses in the circuit as shown in Fig. 10. They can be of the flash lamp bulb type, with a current rating to suit the load to be taken from the power pack with extra provision for any surges that might occur as the condenser charges up.

### High Voltage Transformers

It is unlikely that the amateur will attempt the task of winding a High Voltage Transformer such as would be used to supply a large cathode ray tube, but a few points of High Voltage practice might be touched upon.

Firstly, the peak inverse voltage across a typical television transformer might reach as high as 10,000 volts, so that great

42

care is essential during testing to see that no risk of touching any live circuit is taken.

Secondly, the positive side of such a power pack is usually earthed, so that strain is placed on insulation in many ways. For example the primary of the transformer might easily be earthed via the mains; in such a case the end of the secondary nearest the primary would be the earthed end, thus preventing a large potential difference directly across the insulation separating the windings.

Thirdly air insulation is often relied upon. At high voltages a trace of moisture upon an insulating surface might give rise to sparking or arcing which, while slight at first would rapidly become something approaching a short circuit. For this reason the layers of the secondary are not carried to the end cheeks of the former and as the winding grows outward from the centre the layers are made shorter, giving a pyramidical or stepped effect. In this way, as the potential above earth rises through the winding so does the distance between any earthed object and the winding increase.

Fourthly, the potential difference between the rectifier heater winding and the H.T. winding makes it necessary to have perfect insulation between the windings, a separate heater transformer helping in this respect. Metal rectifiers give very good results for cathode ray tube power supplies.

## Chapter 5

# THE DESIGN AND CONSTRUCTION OF
# LOW FREQUENCY CHOKES

The Low Frequency Choke is used in the power pack to filter out hum from the current supply, for intervalve coupling and in various forms of input and output circuits. Slightly different methods of construction are used dependent upon whether the choke is to carry direct current in the winding as well as A.C.; in a power pack for example, D.C. is flowing whilst in a parallel fed intervalve coupling D.C. would be excluded by a blocking condenser.

The effect of D.C. in the winding is to decrease the incremental permeability of the core material — in practice a laminated core is used as in the transformer — so that the iron saturates more rapidly and the inductance of the choke is lowered. This inductance loss can only be partially countered by arranging to have a small air gap between the sets of laminations in the assembled core.

For chokes carrying A.C. alone, therefore, the laminations are interleaved as are those in a transformer, but for a choke carrying D.C. and A.C. the laminations are assembled with the two sets of stampings one on each side — that is all the E's on one side and all the I's opposite (or all T's together opposite all U's, whichever type of stamping is used), and it will be seen that in the core assembled in this manner there will be three air gaps, one at the end of each limb (Fig. 11). So far as the magnetic circuit is concerned even a tightly clamped butt joint acts as a small air gap, and for correspondingly larger air gaps a piece of thin tissue paper may be inserted between the end of each limb and the opposite laminations. The calculation of the correct air gap for any single case is rather involved, however, and it is recommended that for mixed A.C. and D.C. operation the gap should be decided upon by experiment. As a rough guide it may be said that the close butt joint will do for currents of 5 or even 10 milliamps but for higher currents the gap must be widened by inserting a 0.0005 inch sheet of tissue or more.

## Chokes for Alternating Current Only

These are chokes as used for intervalve coupling, tone control, bass boosting, resonant circuits and audio oscillators, wherever the current feed to the valve is "shunted". The inductance of the choke is given by:—

$$L = \frac{3.2 \times N^2 \times \mu \times A}{l \times 100,000,000}$$

where L is the inductance in henrys, N is the number of turns of wire, $\mu$ is the incremental A.C. permeability of the iron core material, A is the cross sectional area of the winding limb in square inches and l is the length of the magnetic path in inches.

A safe figure to use for $\mu$ is 1,000 unless greater information about the core material is available, and l is measured directly from the laminations. A well-shaped core has the two outer legs only half the width of the inner or winding leg so that the magnetic path is split equally into two, and the length, l, to be measured is the centre line of *one* of these two paths as shown by the dotted line in Fig. 11.

*Example 11*

A choke to possess an inductance of 100 henrys is to be wound on the core of Fig. 11, the dimensions being as shown.

Calculate the number of turns and the size of wire.

l is measured on the core along the path shown and is 6.2 inches. The area of the winding limb is 0.8" x 1" or 0.8 square inches, and as the permeability has been taken as a low figure there is no real need for the 10% allowance to compensate for the thickness of the lamination insulation. The formula becomes, then,

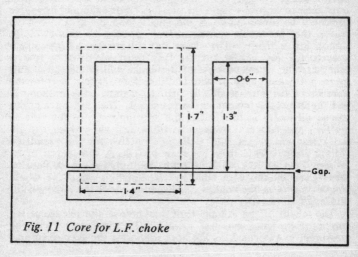

*Fig. 11  Core for L.F. choke*

$$100 = \frac{3.2 \times N^2 \times 1,000 \times 0.8}{6.2 \times 100,000,000}$$

or $N^2 = 24218750$

and $N = 4,920$ turns nearly, say 5,000 turns.

The winding space is $0.6'' \times 1.3''$ and allowing $0.1''$ each way for a former with end cheeks this reduces to an area of $0.5'' \times 1.1''$ or 0.55 square inches, so wire must be used which will wind $1/0.55 \times 5,000$ turns per square inch or 9,090 turns per square inch. Reference to the wire tables shows that S.W.G. 34 enam. winds 10,000 turns per square inch which gives a little room for unevenness in winding.

The choke is finished in the same way as a transformer, with a tightly clamped core and a tape or cloth binding to protect the wire. No provision has here been made for interleaving the windings with paper as it is unlikely that any really dangerous voltage would be set up in such a choke.

## Chokes for Mixed Currents

Where the choke is to carry D.C. as well as A.C. it will scarcely be possible to wind such a high inductance (should it be needed) on such a small core unless the D.C. component is practically negligible. In the first place the wire would need to be of a heavier gauge to carry the current as well as to reduce the D.C. resistance to as low a figure as possible. For example, it may be necessary to use a choke as the anode load for a valve for the reason that a suitable resistance load reduces the anode voltage to too low a figure. The choke will still present a high impedance to the A.C. signal but the D.C. resistance must be low or otherwise the whole purpose of the choke will be defeated. This means a thicker gauge of wire and therefore a larger core, for the number of turns must still be high to maintain the inductance and therefore the impedance to the signal. The simplest way out of the difficulty is to measure the winding space of the core to be used and choose a gauge of wire which when wound to fill the space will give a D.C. resistance suitable for the permitted voltage drop. This may be done by taking the length of an average turn on the winding limb, multiplying the number of turns given by the wire table by this length to find the whole length of wire in the winding, and then to check the resistance of this length in the wire tables.

The length of the average turn is, of course, the average of the length of the first and last turns on the winding and may be measured on the cheek of the core supposing the average turn to be geometrically situated at half the winding depth.

Smoothing chokes also may be wound in this way. Choose a suitable core with a cross sectional area of at least 1 square inch and a window space of at least 2 square inches and decide from the wire tables the gauge of wire which will carry the maximum current safely, using a current density of 1,500 or 2,000 amperes per square inch. Enamelled wire is suitable for the winding and again the layers should not need to be interleaved, the space which would be used by the paper being of greater value if filled with wire.

The gap can be adjusted experimentally by allowing the choke to supply filtered D.C. to a sensitive receiver or amplifier. The core clamping bolts are loosened just sufficiently to allow the sets of laminations to be moved and the space between them is gradually opened until the hum in the loudspeaker, with no signals and the gain control right out, is at a maximum. The gap can then be set with a paper or very thin fibre packing and the core reclamped.

The testing of insulation and general performance of the choke can be modelled on the lines described in Chapter 4.

## Chapter 6

## CHOKES CARRYING DIRECT CURRENT

### Inductance

Chokes of this type are generally required for one of two purposes: (1) Smoothing, and (2) Coupling. In either case, the inductance necessary is based on the impedance which it will have at a certain frequency. For smoothing, this frequency is that of the ripple to be eliminated in smoothing, and for coupling chokes it is the lowest frequency required to be reproduced.

The reactance of an inductance is given by the formula:—

$$X_L = 2\pi fL,$$

where $\pi$ is 3.14, f is the frequency and L the inductance in Henries.

For a smoothing circuit, the condenser reactance must also be known, and this is given by the formula:—

$$X_C = \frac{1,000,000}{2\pi fC}$$

where C is the capacity in Microfarads.

If a smoothing circuit is required to reduce the ripple voltage to 1/40th of that across the reservoir condenser, then the required ratio of reactance of smoothing choke and condenser will be given by

$$\frac{X_C}{X_L} = \frac{1}{40}$$

Assuming an 8 $\mu$F electrolytic condenser is to be used, then its reactance to a ripple voltage of 100 Hz (the predominant frequency from a 50 Hz full wave rectifier) will be

$$\frac{1,000,000}{2 \times 3.14 \times 100 \times 8} = 200 \text{ ohms approx.}$$

Therefore, the reactance of the choke must be 40 x 200 or 8,000 ohms. From the formula, $8,000 = 2\pi 100L$, therefore

$$L = \frac{8,000}{2 \times 3.14 \times 100} = \text{nearly 13 Henries.}$$

In the same way, the inductance can be calculated for any given degree of smoothing.

For a coupling circuit, the inductance must have a given reactance at the lowest frequency to be reproduced (usually taken as 50 Hz for good reproduction, although other values may sometimes be desired, see Chapters 7 and 10). This reactance is usually taken as equal to the valve's anode load impedance.

Thus, if a valve has an optimum load impedance of 10,000 ohms, and is required to handle down to 50 Hz, the value of inductance required in a coupling choke will be

$$L = \frac{10,000}{2 \times 3.14 \times 50} = \text{32 Henries approx.}$$

These values of inductance must not be regarded as obtainable to great accuracy, as the actual value for any given applied A.C. voltage is dependent on the D.C. current flowing at the time, and on the amplitude of the A.C. voltage. Because of this fact, it is always good to allow a little in hand, so that performance will not vary too much if operation should change, due to changes in mains voltage. It would be well to design the chokes in the above examples to have inductances of, say, 15 and 40 Henries respectively.

## Current and Volt Drop

The direct current to be carried by the choke will be fixed by other considerations. In the case of the smoothing choke, by the total current to be taken by the set, and in the case of the coupling choke by the anode current of the valve. As well as being required to give the required inductance at this current, there will usually be an additional requirement that the choke shall not drop more than a certain voltage D.C. across it, due to its resistance.

We now have three factors, which roughly determine how large the choke must be physically. These three factors and the size do not have some simple relation, such as that the size of the choke in, say, cubic inches, is equal to the inductance x current x volt drop. For this reason, Tables 1–5 have been prepared to give a quick means of finding a suitable design.

## Choice of Stampings

There are available, from different manufacturers, hundreds of different shapes and sizes of laminations which could be used for chokes.  Some are definitely wasteful to use, as they would require a heavier or more bulky design to meet certain requirements.  The shapes shown in Figs. 13, 14 and 15 are good shapes

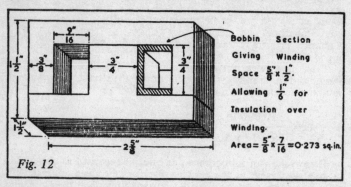

Bobbin Section Giving Winding Space $\frac{5''}{8} \times \frac{1''}{2}$. Allowing $\frac{1''}{6}$ for Insulation over Winding.

Area = $\frac{5''}{8} \times \frac{7}{16} = 0.273$ sq. in.

Fig. 12

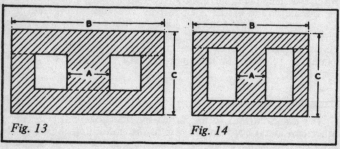

Fig. 13

Fig. 14

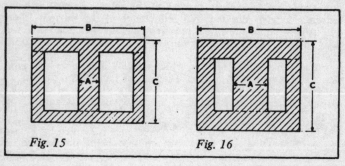

Fig. 15

Fig. 16

to use from the viewpoint of obtaining any required values of inductance, current and volt drop in the smallest or lightest possible design. The shape at Fig. 16 is that known as the "waste-free" (for further details, see Chapter 10). This is also a good shape, especially in the larger sizes, and has the additional advantage that it is often cheaper than other shapes. In the smaller sizes, the disadvantage is that much of the winding space is taken up by the bobbin, due to the shape of the "window".

There is another factor which may influence the choice of laminations. If there is to be a large A.C. voltage across the choke (such as there is in a choke for use between the rectifier and reservoir condenser), then with some designs there will be a loss of inductance due to the fact that the iron core will be saturated with A.C., over and above the effect due to the D.C. A good design for such a case employs a shape such as that at Fig. 13 or Fig. 16, and preferably a fairly large stack, or thickness, of laminations (i.e., if there should be a choice between, say, a 1-inch stack of one size, or a larger stack of a smaller size, then the latter would give best results).

## Use of Tables 1–5

The first table gives a range of 36 different designs, all of which can be wound using a 1½ inch stack of laminations as shown at Fig. 12 allowing for a bobbin made of material 1/16th inch thick. There are six different values of inductance given for each of six different values of direct current flowing. These necessitate a number of different windings, of which the turns and resistance are shown in the table. The D.C. Volt Drop is also tabulated for convenience.

If the value should be outside the range covered by the 36 given, then it may be obtained with the aid of the factors at the bottom of the table. Two examples will best illustrate the use of these factors:—

*Example 12*

An inductance of 200 Henries at 5 milliamps is required. In the table is shown a value of 20 Henries at 50 milliamps. The factors at the bottom show that if the inductance is multiplied by 10 (bottom line), then the resistance and volt drop will each be multiplied by 32, and the turns required by 5.6. Thus, an inductance of 200 Henries at 50 milliamps will have a resistance of 250 x 32 ohms, or 8,000 ohms, giving a volt drop of 12.5 x 32, or 400 volts, and requiring 3,600 x 5.6 or 20,000 turns, approx. Now, from the previous line, it is shown that if the current is divided by 10, then the resistance is divided by 10, and the volt drop by 100, the turns required being divided by 3.2. So the inductance originally required, of 200 Henries at 5 milli-

# Table 1. Values of Current and Inductance for Choke to Dimensions of Fig. 12

| Current milliamps | Inductance Henries | Resistance Ohms | Volts dropped | Turns |
|---|---|---|---|---|
| 10 | 30 | 100 | 1.00 | 2200 |
|  | 50 | 200 | 2.00 | 3200 |
|  | 70 | 350 | 3.50 | 4100 |
|  | 100 | 550 | 5.50 | 5300 |
|  | 150 | 1000 | 10.00 | 7300 |
|  | 200 | 1600 | 16.00 | 9000 |
| 15 | 10 | 30 | 0.45 | 1200 |
|  | 15 | 50 | 0.75 | 1600 |
|  | 20 | 75 | 1.10 | 2000 |
|  | 30 | 140 | 2.10 | 2700 |
|  | 50 | 300 | 4.50 | 3900 |
|  | 70 | 500 | 7.50 | 5000 |
| 20 | 10 | 35 | 0.70 | 1400 |
|  | 15 | 65 | 1.30 | 1800 |
|  | 20 | 100 | 2.00 | 2200 |
|  | 30 | 180 | 3.60 | 3000 |
|  | 50 | 400 | 8.00 | 4500 |
|  | 70 | 650 | 13.00 | 6000 |
| 30 | 10 | 55 | 1.70 | 1700 |
|  | 15 | 100 | 3.00 | 2200 |
|  | 20 | 150 | 4.50 | 2800 |
|  | 30 | 270 | 8.10 | 3700 |
|  | 50 | 600 | 18.00 | 5700 |
|  | 70 | 1000 | 30.00 | 7300 |
| 50 | 10 | 90 | 4.50 | 2100 |
|  | 15 | 160 | 8.00 | 2900 |
|  | 20 | 250 | 12.50 | 3600 |
|  | 30 | 450 | 23.00 | 4800 |
|  | 50 | 1000 | 50.00 | 6500 |
|  | 70 | 1600 | 80.00 | 9000 |
| 70 | 5 | 45 | 3.00 | 1500 |
|  | 7 | 75 | 5.00 | 2000 |
|  | 10 | 120 | 8.50 | 2500 |
|  | 15 | 230 | 16.00 | 3400 |
|  | 20 | 350 | 24.00 | 4100 |
|  | 30 | 650 | 45.00 | 6000 |
| $\times \div 10$ |  | $\times \div 10$ | $\times \div 100$ | $\times \div 3.2$ |
|  | $\times \div 10$ | $\times \div 32$ | $\times \div 32$ | $\times \div 5.6$ |

52

**Table 2. Values of Resistance and Turns compared to those in Table 1 for cores shaped as at Fig. 13**

| Dimensions to Fig. 13 (inches) | Winding area (sq inches) | Core stack (inches) | Turns factor | Resistance factor |
|---|---|---|---|---|
| A = 0.500<br>B = 1.750<br>C = 1.000 | 0.095 | 0.500<br>0.750<br>1.000 | X 2.8<br>X 2.1<br>X 1.7 | X 12.0<br>X 7.5<br>X 5.5 |
| A = 0.625<br>B = 2.0625<br>C = 1.250 | 0.170 | 0.625<br>0.875<br>1.250 | X 2.2<br>X 1.7<br>X 1.3 | X 4.8<br>X 3.2<br>X 2.2 |
| A = 0.750<br>B = 2.625<br>C = 1.500 | 0.275 | 0.750<br>1.125<br>1.500 | X 1.7<br>X 1.3<br>As in Table 1 | X 2.3<br>X 1.4 |
| A = 1.000<br>B = 3.500<br>C = 2.000 | 0.550 | 1.000<br>1.500<br>2.000 | X 1.2<br>÷ 1.2<br>÷ 1.5 | ÷ 1.4<br>÷ 2.3<br>÷ 3.2 |
| A = 1.250<br>B = 4.375<br>C = 2.500 | 0.920 | 1.250<br>1.875<br>2.500 | ÷ 1.1<br>÷ 1.5<br>÷ 1.9 | ÷ 3.3<br>÷ 5.5<br>÷ 7.5 |
| A = 1.500<br>B = 5.250<br>C = 3.000 | 1.375 | 1.500<br>2.250<br>3.000 | ÷ 1.5<br>÷ 2.0<br>÷ 2.4 | ÷ 6.5<br>÷ 10.0<br>÷ 14.0 |

amps, will have a resistance of 8,000 ÷ 10, or 800 ohms, giving a volt drop of 400 ÷ 100, or 4 volts, and requiring 20,000 ÷ 3.2, or about 6,300 turns.

*Example 13*

To design an inductance of 1 Henry at 1 amp on this core size: in the table an inductance of 100 Henries at 10 milliamps is given as having a resistance of 550 ohms and requiring 5,300 turns. 1 amp is 1,000 milliamps, or 100 x 10 mA. From the factor given, if the current is multiplied by 10, then the resistance will be 10 times, using 3.2 times the turns. So, if the current is multiplied by 100, then the resistance will be 100 times, and the turns will need to be 3.2 x 3.2, or 10 times. As the inductance is to be divided by 100, the resistance due to this change will be divided by 32 x 32, or 1,000, and the turns required will be divided by 5.6 x 5.6, or 32. Thus, the values given in the table for 100 Henries at 10 milliamps can be converted into those for 1 Henry at 1 amp as follows:—

$$\text{Resistance} = 550 \times \frac{100}{1,000} = 55 \text{ ohms}$$

**Table 3. Values of Resistance and Turns compared to those in Table 1 for cores shaped as at Fig. 14**

| Dimensions to Fig. 14 (inches) | Winding area (sq inches) | Core stack (inches) | Turns factor | Resistance factor |
|---|---|---|---|---|
| A = 0.500<br>B = 2.000<br>C = 1.500 | 0.33 | 0.500<br>0.750<br>1.000 | X 3.2<br>X 2.3<br>X 1.9 | X 4.8<br>X 3.0<br>X 2.1 |
| A = 0.625<br>B = 2.500<br>C = 1.875 | 0.56 | 0.625<br>0.875<br>1.250 | X 2.4<br>X 1.9<br>X 1.4 | X 2.0<br>X 1.4<br>X 1.1 |
| A = 0.750<br>B = 3.000<br>C = 2.250 | 0.86 | 0.750<br>1.125<br>1.500 | X 1.9<br>X 1.4<br>X 1.1 | X 1.0<br>÷ 1.7<br>÷ 2.3 |
| A = 1.000<br>B = 4.000<br>C = 3.000 | 1.65 | 1.000<br>1.500<br>2.000 | X 1.3<br>X 1.0<br>÷ 1.3 | ÷ 3.0<br>÷ 5.0<br>÷ 7.0 |
| A = 1.250<br>B = 5.000<br>C = 3.750 | 2.6 | 1.250<br>1.875<br>2.500 | X 1.0<br>÷ 1.4<br>÷ 1.7 | ÷ 7.0<br>÷ 11.0<br>÷ 15.0 |
| A = 1.500<br>B = 6.000<br>C = 4.500 | 3.8 | 1.500<br>2.250<br>3.000 | ÷ 1.3<br>÷ 1.7<br>÷ 2.2 | ÷ 11.0<br>÷ 20.0<br>÷ 30.0 |

$$\text{Volt Drop} = 5.5 \times \frac{10,000}{1,000} = 55 \text{ volts}$$

$$\text{Turns} = 5,300 \times \frac{10}{32} = 1,650$$

Thus, it is seen that the table can be used to find the necessary value of resistance and turns to give any inductance and direct current on this core size. If the resistance and volt drop are of a suitable value, then this size could be used, if laminations are available, and when the coil is wound, it is necessary to find the air gap required from the tables in Chapter 9.

If the resistance or volt drop obtained in this way is either (1) unnecessarily low, or (2) too high, then an appropriate core size may now be chosen directly from reference to one of Tables 2–5, which list a variety of shapes, sizes and stacks, together with a factor showing the relation between resistance and turns for a design on this size as compared to that having the same inductance at the same D.C. on the size shown in Fig. 12 and tabulated in Table 1.

**Table 4. Values of Resistance and Turns compared to those in Table 1 for cores shaped as at Fig. 15**

| Dimensions to Fig. 15 (inches) | Winding area (sq inches) | Core stack (inches) | Turns factor | Resistance factor |
|---|---|---|---|---|
| A = 0.500<br>B = 2.750<br>C = 2.000 | 1.00 | 0.500<br>0.750<br>1.000<br>1.500 | X 3.4<br>X 2.5<br>X 2.0<br>X 1.5 | X 2.5<br>X 1.5<br>X 1.0<br>÷ 1.5 |
| A = 0.625<br>B = 3.4375<br>C = 2.500 | 1.65 | 0.625<br>0.875<br>1.250<br>1.875 | X 2.6<br>X 2.0<br>X 1.5<br>X 1.1 | X 1.1<br>÷ 1.4<br>÷ 2.2<br>÷ 3.5 |
| A = 0.750<br>B = 4.125<br>C = 3.000 | 2.40 | 0.750<br>1.125<br>1.500<br>2.250 | X 2.0<br>X 1.5<br>X 1.2<br>÷ 1.1 | ÷ 1.7<br>÷ 3.0<br>÷ 4.0<br>÷ 6.5 |
| A = 1.000<br>B = 5.500<br>C = 4.000 | 4.40 | 1.000<br>1.500<br>2.000<br>3.000 | X 1.4<br>X 1.0<br>÷ 1.3<br>÷ 1.6 | ÷ 5.0<br>÷ 8.5<br>÷ 12.0<br>÷ 18.0 |
| A = 1.250<br>B = 6.875<br>C = 5.000 | 6.80 | 1.250<br>1.875<br>2.500<br>3.750 | X 1.1<br>÷ 1.3<br>÷ 1.6<br>÷ 2.1 | ÷ 10 0<br>÷ 18.0<br>÷ 25.0<br>÷ 40.0 |

It will be realized that it is unimportant whether the laminations take the form of E's and I's, or of T's and U's, so long as they fit together to make approximately the shape shown. If a stamping is available which does not fit all the dimensions shown, the best method is to see which shape it most nearly resembles. This can readily be found by holding a lamination in one hand and this book in the other, and by holding them at different distances from the eye so that the outline of the lamination and the figure in the book appear the same size. It will then be easy to see which of the four shapes given most closely correspond to the actual stamping.

To find the stack required, use the resistance factor column to find what stack of the given shape whose dimensions B and C most closely correspond with the actual stack which is required. Then, to find the turns factor, use the size whose dimension A is the same as the actual stamping, and of the same stack as nearly as possible. Generally it will be seen that when the shape which is nearest to the actual is found, the size as judged by the nearest correspondency of dimensions B and C will also give the right value for dimension A.

**Table 5. Values of Resistance and Turns**
compared to those in Table 1 for cores shaped as at Fig. 16

| Dimensions to Fig. 16 (inches) | Winding area (sq inches) | Core stack (inches) | Turns factor | Resistance factor |
|---|---|---|---|---|
| A = 0.500<br>B = 1.500<br>C = 1.250 | 0.078 | 0.500<br>0.750<br>1.000 | X 2.8<br>X 2.1<br>X 1.7 | X 13.0<br>X 8.0<br>X 6.0 |
| A = 0.625<br>B = 1.875<br>C = 1.5625 | 0.150 | 0.625<br>0.875<br>1.250 | X 2.1<br>X 1.7<br>X 1.3 | X 4.8<br>X 3.3<br>X 2.3 |
| A = 0.750<br>B = 2.250<br>C = 1.875 | 0.250 | 0.750<br>1.125<br>1.500 | X 1.7<br>X 1.3<br>As in Table 1 | X 2.2<br>X 1.4 |
| A = 1.000<br>B = 3.000<br>C = 2.500 | 0.470 | 1.000<br>1.500<br>2.000 | X 1.2<br>÷ 1.1<br>÷ 1.4 | ÷ 1.3<br>÷ 2.1<br>÷ 2.8 |
| A = 1.250<br>B = 3.750<br>C = 3.125 | 0.875 | 1.250<br>1.875<br>2.500 | ÷ 1.1<br>÷ 1.5<br>÷ 1.9 | ÷ 2.9<br>÷ 4.8<br>÷ 7.5 |
| A = 1.500<br>B = 4.500<br>C = 3.750 | 1.300 | 1.500<br>2.250<br>3.000 | ÷ 1.4<br>÷ 1.9<br>÷ 2.3 | ÷ 7.0<br>÷ 11.0<br>÷ 15.0 |

*Example 14*

Continuing the case of the 200 Henry 5 milliamp inductance of Example 12, suppose that a 4 volt drop is unnecessarily low. Assume that a drop of 20–25 volts can be allowed. This means that the resistance and volt drop can be 5 or 6 times that of the design given on the size of Fig. 12. From Table 2 we find that a lamination of this shape, having overall dimensions 1″ x 1¾″, will give a design having a volt drop of 5.5 x 4, or 22 volts, using a 1″ stack. Or a larger one of the same shape, having dimensions 1¼″ x 2³⁄₁₆″, and ⅝″ stack, gives volt drop of 4.8 x 4, or nearly 20 volts. Using the shape of Fig. 14 from Table 3 we find a size having overall dimensions 2″ x 1½″ and stack ½″, which gives the same drop. This would obviously be the most compact size for this particular design. There is another alternative in Table 5, using a ⅝″ stack of a lamination having outside dimensions 1⁹⁄₁₆″ x 1⅛″, and giving a volt drop of nearly 20. In each case the number of turns required is calculated by multiplying the factor in the Turns Factor column by the number obtained from Table 1, i.e. 6,300.

*Example 15*

Continuing the case of the 1 Henry 1 amp choke of Example

13, suppose that 55 volts is much too great, and that a limit of 5 volts has been set. Then a size must be chosen which gives a division factor of 55/5 or 11. The largest size on Table 2 gives 14; there are two in Table 3 that give 11, one in Table 4 that gives 12, and one in Table 5 that gives 11 — a choice of five sizes. As this is a large-size choke, the best shape is the "waste-free", giving a 2¼" stack of laminations 3¾" x 4½". The turns required will be 1,650 ÷ 1.9, or about 900.

For the method of finding wire gauge in these examples, see Chapter 15.

As well as the variation of inductance mentioned already as due to variation of current and A.C. voltage, the D.C. resistance cannot be expected to conform to close limits either, because of slight variations in wire gauge from the standard.

# Chapter 7

# INTER-VALVE TRANSFORMERS CARRYING DIRECT CURRENT

## Primary Inductance and Resistance

Tables 1-5 may be used to find the inductance of any given number of turns on the sizes given, but the resistance calculated from these tables will be increased, and with it the volt drop.

Suppose that the primary consists of 3,000 turns on the second size listed in Table 3, i.e., a $\frac{5}{8}''$ stack of laminations with dimensions $A = \frac{3}{8}''$, $B = 2\frac{1}{2}''$, $C = 1\frac{1}{8}''$ (see Fig. 14), and that the primary current is 10 milliamps. From Table 3 we see that 3,000 turns is 2.4 times as many as would be required on the size given in Table 1 to have the same inductance at the same current. This means that $3,000 \div 2.4$, or 1,250 turns, would be required on this larger size. Now, referring to Table 1, at 10 milliamps there is no number of turns as low as 1,250, but the factor at the bottom for multiplying or dividing the inductance by 10 is 5.6. Multiplying 1,250 by 5.6 gives 7,000 turns, which does fall within the range given by the table. 5,300 turns give an inductance of 100 Henries at 10 mA, and 7,300 turns give an inductance of 150 Henries at 10 mA, so 7,000 turns will give an inductance of about 140 Henries at 10 mA. Now, dividing by 5.6, this means that 1,250 turns on this size, or 3,000 turns on the actual size, will give 14 Henries at 10 mA.

As a choke, the 7,000-turn winding would have a resistance of about 900 ohms (see Table 1, between 550 and 1,000, for 5,300 and 7,300 turns respectively). By the factor at the bottom of Table 1, the resistance of the 1,250 turns will be $900 \div 32 = 28$ ohms approx. From the resistance factor in Table 3 for the actual size, the resistance of a choke having the 3,000 turns as specified would be $28 \times 2 = 56$ ohms. But, in this case, the primary will only occupy one-half or perhaps one-third of the total winding space. This means that its resistance will be increased by two or three times to 112 or 168 ohms. This, then, allows the remaining one-half to two-thirds of the space for the secondary. If a very high step-up is used, needing a very large number of turns on the secondary, then even less than one-third of the space may have to do for the primary.

## Choice of Size

Of the sizes shown in the tables, the one already mentioned is the best for an inter-valve transformer for direct coupling. It gives the greatest possible step-up in any given inter-valve circuit,

58

consistent with a balanced frequency response. If a smaller size is used, then either step-up must be sacrificed or the frequency band will be higher up the scale, giving a "thin" quality reproduction. If a larger size is used, then again step-up must be reduced, or else the frequency band will be moved down the scale, giving a "woofy" reproduction.

## Choice of Ratio and Turns

The response curves shown in Figs. 17 and 18 show various shapes of the frequency response obtained with the ratios and turns given in Table 6. For all these curves, the design is taken as being for a transformer to work with a valve having an anode current of 10 milliamps, and an anode impedance (*not* the optimum anode load) of 7,000 ohms. This would be a typical medium slope triode.

In Fig. 17 the same ratio is achieved with three different

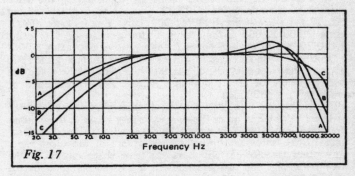

*Fig. 17*

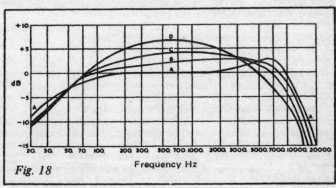

*Fig. 18*

**Table 6. Conditions required for response curves in Figs. 17, 18**

| Ratio | Primary turns | Secondary turns | Response curve | Referred impedance |
|-------|---------------|-----------------|----------------|--------------------|
| 3:1 | 4000 | 12000 | { A A, Fig. 17<br>{ A A A, Fig. 18 | 63000 |
| 3:1 | 3000 | 9000 | B B, Fig. 17 | 63000 |
| 3:1 | 2000 | 6000 | C C, Fig. 17 | 63000 |
| 4:1 | 3000 | 12000 | B, Fig. 18 | 112000 |
| 5:1 | 2400 | 12000 | C, Fig. 18 | 175000 |
| 6:1 | 2000 | 12000 | D, Fig. 18 | 250000 |

numbers of turns. Curve AA is the result of using 4,000/12,000 turns; curve BB with 3,000/9,000; and curve CC with 2,000/6,000.

In Fig. 18 different turns ratios are used, having the same number of secondary turns, 12,000. Curve AAA is obtained as in Fig. 17 for a 3/1 using 4,000/12,000; curve B is for ratio of 4/1, using 3,000/12,000 turns; curve C for a ratio of 5/1, using 2,400/12,000 turns; and curve D for a ratio of 6/1, using 2,000/12,000 turns. In this case, it will be seen that increasing the ratio narrows the frequency band, but that it is kept balanced about a mid-frequency of about 600 or 700 Hz. For reproduction of music this is a good ideal.

To enable the information given in these curves to be applied to other cases when other types of valve may be used, the column "referred impedance" is given. This is simply the anode impedance of the valve multiplied by the square of the turns ratio. Any other transformer will have the same shape cut-off at the high frequency end of its response if it has the same number of secondary turns, and the same referred impedance as that given in the table. The shape of the cut-off at the low frequency end of the response depends upon the primary inductance and the anode impedance of the valve, as stated in Chapter 6.

*Example 16*

To estimate the best ratio and turns for use with a valve having an anode impedance of 2,500 ohms and an anode current of 20 milliamps.

The widest frequency range is obtained with the use of 12,000 turns on the secondary, and with a referred impedance of 63,000 ohms gives a response cut-off at the top end as shown in curves A (Figs. 17 and 18). To make 2,500 ohms refer as 63,000, the square of the turns ratio must be 63,000/2,500 or about 25/1. This gives a turns ratio of 5/1. Then the primary turns will need to be 2,400. Using Tables 1 and 3, as before, this winding will have an inductance of about 6 Henries with 20 mA flowing. This makes the cut-off frequency at the low end that at which 6 Henries has a reactance of 2,500 ohms. $X_L = 2\pi fL$, i.e., $2,500 = 2 \times 3.14 \times 6 \times f$, therefore,

$$f = \frac{2,500}{2 \times 3.14 \times 6} = 65 \text{ Hz, approx.}$$

This means that the point where the response is 3 dB down from level is at 65 Hz. Curve A shows this as 50 Hz.

Thus this case, using a 5/1 or 2,400/12,000 will give an L.F. response not quite so good as that in curves A, while the H.F. response will be identical. Using the same turns on the next size a ¾ inch stack of the next larger laminations listed, will have the effect of bringing the whole response down by a ratio of about 5/6. This will about balance the frequency response.

## Example 17

To estimate the best arrangement to use with a valve having an anode impedance of 10,000 ohms, and an anode current of 5 mA.

Using the same reference impedance, the square of the ratio needs to be 63,000/10,000 or 6.3/1. This gives a turns ratio of about 2.5/1, and so the primary turns would be 4,800.

To work out the primary inductance, as before; 4,800 turns on the best size as already stated have the same inductance for the same current as $4,800 \div 2.4$ or 2,000 turns on the size of Fig. 12. There is no section of Table 1 for 5 mA, but there is for 50 mA, and the factor at the bottom shows that multiplying or dividing current by 10, multiplies or divides turns by 3.2. So the same inductance with 50 mA, instead of 5 mA, would need 2,000 × 3.2, or 6,400 turns. This closely corresponds with the figure for 50 Henries, and the error introduced by assuming that 4,800 turns on our actual size will produce an inductance of 50 Henries at 5 mA, is quite small. To find the 3 dB frequency: $X_L = 2\pi fL$; $10,000 = 2 \times 3 \cdot 14 \times f \times 50$, or

$$f = \frac{10,000}{2 \times 3.14 \times 50} = 32 \text{ Hz.}$$

This is rather better than necessary, and it will be found that an inductance of 32 H will bring the 3 dB point to 50 Hz. Working back, we find this needs less than 4,000 turns on the actual primary. If 4,000 turns is used, the ratio is 3/1, and the referred impedance will be 9 × 10,000 = 90,000 ohms. This will give a H.F. cut off mid-way between that for curves A and B in Fig. 18, whilst maintaining the L.F. cut-off a little better than that for curve A. This will be reasonably well balanced, giving a range from about 45 to 10,000 Hz.

## Method of Winding and Connection

With any inter-valve transformer it is important to keep the winding capacities to the lowest possible figure, as these introduce further loss of high frequencies. The secondary, being the winding at the highest impedance, is the most important in this respect. For this reason the following method should be adopted.

The secondary should be wound on first, so as to have the smallest diameter, and the inside, or start, of the winding should be the end which is eventually connected to the grid of the next valve. This means that the outside, or finish, will be connected either to the grid bias or earth.

After insulation has been placed between windings, the primary will be wound on. This may be of the same or of different gauge from the secondary (see Chapter 15). The inside, or start, should be connected to H.T. supply or decoupling, while the outside, or finish of this winding should be connected to anode.

This practice will always be found to give the best results.

# Chapter 8

# OUTPUT TRANSFORMER FOR SINGLE VALVE

### Turns and Impedance Ratio

The purpose of this type of transformer is to match the impedance of a loudspeaker, or group of loudspeakers, to the optimum load of the valve. That is, the transformer has the effect of transforming the impedance of the speaker so that the impedance which it presents in the primary winding is equal to the optimum load of the output valve.

It is well known that the impedance ratio of a transformer is equal to the square of the turns ratio.

### Impedance/Turns Relationship

This depends on the D.C. current flowing in the primary, on the size and shape, and on the lowest frequency required. To make calculation easier, if the actual D.C. current flowing in the primary is referred to a theoretical 1,000 ohms winding, then the turns for such a winding can readily be found, and from that the turns in the actual windings determined. Using this reference, the current in this winding will bear a relationship to the maximum output power which will vary very little, although widely different types of valve may be used.

Table 7 gives a series of reference figures. For each value of current referred to 1,000 ohm winding, is given two figures for the turns in a 1,000 ohm winding: one for general use, giving a low frequency cut-off of 50 Hz, and the other for special use when a circuit is used for speech only, giving a low frequency cut-off of 200 Hz. For each value of current is given an approximate figure of maximum output. This may be found useful if some of the valve data is not obtainable (e.g., the optimum load). For each value of current and cut-off is given the approximate percentage loss due to winding resistance.

### Choice of Size

The figures in Table 7 are for the same core dimensions as those shown in Fig. 12. In practice, for an output transformer it will be better from the constructional viewpoint if the stack is less than twice the A dimension, preferably equal to it. The chief factor in determining size is the amount of power that can be allowed as loss in the transformer. The appropriate loss factors for other sizes may be found from the figures given by multiplying or dividing by the Resistance Factor given in Tables 2—5

**Table 7. Umpedance/Turns Relationship for Core of Size shown in Fig. 12**

| D.C. referred to 1000 Ω | 50 Hz cut-off | | 200 Hz cut-off | | |
| | Turns for 10000 Ω | Series loss | Turns for 1000 Ω | Series loss | Max power |
|---|---|---|---|---|---|
| 50 | 900 | 7% | 310 | 1.0% | 800 mW |
| 70 | 1100 | 9% | 380 | 1.3% | 1.5 W |
| 100 | 1300 | 13% | 450 | 2.0% | 3.0 W |
| 150 | 1600 | 20% | 550 | 3.0% | 7.0 W |
| 200 | 1900 | 28% | 650 | 4.0% | 12.0 W |

for the appropriate shape and size.

Having chosen a suitable size, the number of turns for a 1,000 ohm winding can be found by use of the Turns Factor in the same table, applied to the value given in Table 7.

*Example 18*

Calculate the turns required to match a 15 ohm speaker to a valve having an optimum load of 4,500 ohms, and an anode current of 48 milliamps for general use on music and speech. It should be at least 90% efficient.

If 48 milliamps are flowing in a winding of impedance 4,500 ohms, then the equivalent in a 1,000 ohms winding will be

$$48 \times \sqrt{\frac{4,500}{1,000}} = 100 \text{ mA approx.}$$

From this value in Table 7 it is seen that on the size shown in Fig. 12 for a 50 Hz cut-off, 1,300 turns for 1,000 winding give a loss of 13%.

To have at least 90% efficiency, the loss must be at most 100 − 90 = 10%. This means that a size must be chosen with a dividing Resistance Factor of at least 1.3. The following sizes satisfy this:—

| Table No. | Dimensions | | | Stack | Turns factor | Resistance factor |
| | A | B | C | | | |
|---|---|---|---|---|---|---|
| 2 | 1.000 | 3.5000 | 2.500 | 1.000 | × 1.2 | ÷ 1.4 |
| 3 | 1.125 | 3.0000 | 2.250 | 0.750 | × 1.4 | ÷ 1.7 |
| 4 | 0.875 | 3.4375 | 2.500 | 0.625 | × 2.0 | ÷ 1.4 |
| 5 | 1.000 | 3.0000 | 2.500 | 1.000 | × 1.2 | ÷ 1.3 |

It will be noticed that there is little difference in size, and therefore there is not much to choose as to which is the best to use. Assume that a size similar to the one from Table 3 is available, then the loss will be $13 \div 1.7 = 7.6\%$ and the efficiency $100 - 7.6 = 92.4\%$. The turns for a 1,000 ohm winding will be $1.4 \times 1,300 = 1,800$ approx. Then the turns for a 4,500 ohm winding will be

$$1,800 \times \sqrt{\frac{4,500}{1,000}} = 3,800.$$

The turns for the 15 ohm winding will be

$$1,800 \times \sqrt{\frac{15}{1,000}} = 220.$$

Thus the transformer will require a primary of 3,800 turns and a secondary of 220 turns.

*Example 19*

The only details known about an output valve are that with 450 volts H.T. it should give about 12 watts output, taking an anode current of 120 milliamps. It is required to match a horn type speaker for use on speech only, with an efficiency of about 90%. The speech coil impedance is 4.5 ohms.

From Table 7 it is seen that 12 watts corresponds to a current referred to a 1,000 ohms winding of 200 mA. The actual current is 120 mA, so the optimum load must be

$$1,000 \times \frac{200^2}{120^2} = 2,800 \text{ ohms.}$$

Also the loss for a 200 Hz cut-off type on this size is only 4%. As the efficiency is only required to be 90%, the loss can be up to 10%. This means a smaller size can be used, which may facilitate fitting the transformer into the horn housing. Thus the resistance can be multiplied by 2.5 (but not more). It will be seen that a ¾ inch stack of the same lamination will give a resistance factor of × 2.3. An alternative is found in Table 5 using a ¾ inch stack of a similar size. In either case the turns factor is × 1.7, so the calculation of turns in this case will be the same whichever is chosen.

From Table 7 the turns for a 1,000 winding are 650. So for this size the turns will be $1.7 \times 650 = 1,100$. The turns for a 2,800 ohms winding will be

$$1,100 \times \sqrt{\frac{2,800}{1,000}} = 1,850.$$

The turns for the 4.5 ohm winding will be

$$1,850 \times \sqrt{\frac{4.5}{2,800}} = 74.$$

The ratio in this case is $1,850/74 = 25/1$.

### Special Precaution for 200 Hz Cut-off

When an amplifier is to be used under conditions required to operate a loudspeaker having a 200 Hz cut-off (i.e., a horn type), there are two precautions necessary: (1) To see that no signal or any considerable amplitude reaches the speaker. This is to prevent damage to the speaker itself, or the introduction of distortion by it due to receiving frequencies which it is not designed to handle. (2) To see that no signal of a lower frequency which may be present in the amplifier causes distortion to frequencies which do reach the loudspeaker.

This second requirement means either that the output of the amplifier must be correctly matched at these frequencies although arrangement is made so that they do not reach the speaker, or that arrangement must be made to ensure that these frequencies do not reach the output stage of the amplifier.

Chapter 10 shows a way in which matching can be maintained with a push-pull stage output by means of a series condenser, but this is not applicable to the cases considered in this section. It is therefore necessary, when using a 200 Hz cut-off type, to take steps to ensure that there is a similar cut-off in the amplifier, somewhere before the output stage. This should take the form of a coupling condenser whose impedance at 200 Hz is equal to that of the grid leak following it.

# Chapter 9

## AIR GAP DETERMINATION

With each of the types of component considered in Chapters 6–8 there is D.C. flowing in one of the windings which has a tendency to saturate the iron core. For this reason an air gap is employed, instead of laminating the transformers in the manner required for types considered in Chapters 10–12.

For any given case, too small an air gap will result in the magnetic flux due to the D.C. component producing saturation, while too large a gap will cause loss of inductance because of the magnetizing current necessary to drive the A.C. component of flux across the air gap.

The chief factor which determines the best air gap for any given example is the total effective D.C. magnetizing force, which may be expressed in ampere-turns — that is to say, the current in amperes multiplied by the turns in the winding. The type of transformer iron used, and the length of iron path (see Fig. 19), both have a slight effect upon the best gap, and on the resulting inductance. As the effect of different iron is so slight, the use of more expensive irons is not considered worth the extra cost in general, so the only iron considered here is ordinary grade transformer iron (usual lamination thickness about 0.016″).

All the figures in Chapters 6–8 for Current and Inductance assume that the air gap is adjusted to the best size. Table 8 gives

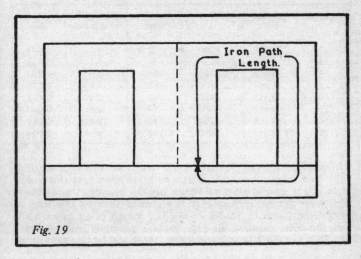

*Fig. 19*

# Table 8. Air Gaps for Components Carrying D.C.

| Magnetizing Ampere turns | Air gap Iron path length (in) 2 inches | Air gap Iron path length (in) 20 inches |
|---|---|---|
| 10 | 0.00033 | — |
| 15 | 0.00048 | — |
| 20 | 0.00063 | — |
| 30 | 0.0009 | — |
| 50 | 0.0014 | — |
| 70 | 0.0019 | 0.0023 |
| 100 | 0.0025 | 0.0032 |
| 150 | 0.0037 | 0.0046 |
| 200 | 0.0047 | 0.006 |
| 300 | 0.0068 | 0.0085 |
| 500 | 0.0105 | 0.0135 |
| 700 | 0.0145 | 0.018 |
| 1000 | 0.02 | 0.025 |
| 1500 | 0.028 | 0.036 |
| 2000 | 0.037 | 0.047 |
| 3000 | 0.055 | 0.067 |
| 5000 | 0.083 | 0.105 |
| 7000 | 0.11 | 0.14 |
| 10000 | 0.155 | 0.195 |
| 15000 | 0.22 | 0.28 |
| 20000 | 0.29 | 0.36 |

| Example No. | Current D.C. | Turns | Ampere turns | Iron path length (in) | Air gap (in) |
|---|---|---|---|---|---|
| 12 | 5 mA | 6300 | 31.5 | 4.1 | 0.001 |
| 13 | 1 A | 1650 | 1650 | 4.1 | 0.035 |
| 14 | 5 mA | 20000 | 100 | 4.0 | 0.027 |
| 15 | 1 A | 900 | 900 | 9.0 | 0.021 |
| 16 | 20 mA | 2400 | 48 | 6.0 | 0.015 |
| 17 | 5 mA | 4000 | 20 | 5.0 | 0.007 |
| 18 | 48 mA | 3800 | 183 | 6.0 | 0.005 |
| 19 | 120 mA | 1850 | 222 | 4.1 or 4.5 | 0.006 |

the approximate gap lengths for different values of ampere turns. Only two values of length of iron path are shown, as this has so little effect, and so practical values will fall between those shown, which are respectively smaller and greater than all the sizes of lamination listed in Tables 2—5. The length of air gap given is half the total required air gap, because generally, with either T and U, or E and I type laminations, there will be two gaps in the iron circuit. If a type is used which only utilises one gap in the iron circuit, then twice the figure given in Table 8 should be taken.

The gaps listed include very small values, which can in practice only be obtained by squeezing the two sections of laminations together without any gap spacing material. For larger gaps, pieces of insulating material of the required thickness may be inserted in the gaps to maintain uniform spacing of the whole cross section of the core.

If equipment is available to test the component for inductance under operating value of D.C. current (as outlined in Chapter 14), then the values given in Table 8 will give a good starting point, which will usually be found within a close percentage of the actual optimum. Deviations will generally be due to practical variations on account of difficulties in clamping up. If such equipment is not available, then care should be taken to produce as near to the specified gap as is possible, making slight allowances if the edges of the laminations should have been slightly burred in stamping.

To give examples of the use of this table, and to complete the examples given in previous sections, those numbered 12—19 are listed, with a repitition of current flowing and turns.

# Chapter 10

## PUSH-PULL OUTPUT AND LOUDSPEAKER TRANSFORMERS

### Choice of Size

For this purpose the best shape is that known as the "Waste-free". The dimensions are set out in Fig. 20, referred to the width of the centre limb. The small diagram shows the way the laminations are stamped from the sheet so there is no waste portion. It will be seen that this method of cutting can only be employed to make laminations of the E and I type. However, from the point of view of efficiency, frequency band, etc., it is obvious that a core of the same shape constructed from laminations of the T and U type will be equally good.

Table 9 gives data for a series of easily obtainable sizes, in different stacks. It shows the turns for a 1,000 winding which give a transformer of maximum efficiency at a frequency of 400–1,000 Hz. The section headed "Maximum power, Watts", shows the maximum power that can be handled by the transformer under this condition at two frequencies, 50 Hz and 200 Hz without introducing serious distortion. The figures

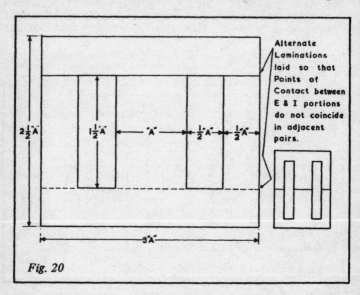

Fig. 20

**Table 9.  Impedance/Turns Relationship, Maximum Power and L.F. Cut-off for Maximum Efficiency at Mid-band Condition**

| Dimension A, Fig. 20 | Core stack | Turns for 1000 Ω | Maximum power Watts | | Mid-band losses | L.F. cut-off Hz |
|---|---|---|---|---|---|---|
| | | | 50 Hz | 200 Hz | | |
| 0.75 { | 0.75 | 750 | (1.75) | 28 | 11.5% | 90 |
| | 1.25 | 660 | (3.50) | 56 | 10.0% | 80 |
| | 1.50 | 500 | (5.25) | 84 | 9.3% | 70 |
| 1.00 { | 1.00 | 770 | ( 7) | 110 | 8.5% | 65 |
| | 1.50 | 670 | (12) | 190 | 7.4% | 60 |
| | 2.00 | 500 | (17) | 270 | 6.8% | 55 |
| 1.25 { | 1.25 | 790 | (18) | 280 | 6.0% | 53 |
| | 1.75 | 700 | 28 | 450 | 5.4% | 46 |
| | 2.50 | 620 | 45 | 700 | 4.8% | 43 |
| 1.50 { | 1.50 | 800 | 40 | 650 | 4.8% | 39 |
| | 2.25 | 720 | 70 | 1100 | 4.3% | 35 |
| | 3.00 | 640 | 100 | 1600 | 4.0% | 32 |

in the 50 Hz column in brackets are so shown because they cannot be applied at that frequency under maximum mid-band efficiency condition, because they are below cut-off, and hence the inductive load on the output valve would introduce distortion by mismatching.  However, if appropriate factors from Table 10 are used to reduce cut-off to 50 Hz or below, the corresponding factors from the same table may be used to obtain

**Table 10.  Factors for other impedance/turns relationships and for change from standard transformer iron to Radiometal**

| | Turns X | Maximum power X | Mid-band losses X | L.F. cut-off ÷ |
|---|---|---|---|---|
| Factors for turns referred to Table 9 | 1.25 | 1.50 | 1.10 | 1.50 |
| | 1.50 | 2.25 | 1.35 | 2.25 |
| | 1.75 | 3.00 | 1.70 | 3.00 |
| | 2.00 | 4.00 | 2.20 | 4.00 |
| | 2.50 | 6.25 | 3.20 | 6.25 |
| | 3.00 | 9.00 | 4.60 | 9.00 |
| | 3.50 | 12.00 | 6.10 | 12.00 |
| | 4.00 | 16.00 | 8.00 | 16.00 |
| Factor for change to Radiometal | ÷ 1.3 | X 2.3 | ÷ 1,7 | equal |

the maximum output at 50 Hz in conjunction with the figures in brackets.

Table 10 shows how increased power and a lower-cut off frequency may be obtained when the impedance/turns relationship is increased above the figure given for any size in Table 9, together with the increases in losses, from which may be deduced the efficiency obtainable.

The factors at the bottom of Table 10 show how the figures can be improved by the use of Radiometal laminations instead of standard transformer iron.

For designs of both Class A Push-Pull Output and Loudspeaker matching transformers, the total winding space occupied by the primary winding should be approximately equal to that occupied by the secondary.

For any type of Q.P.P. output stage, the most efficient disposition of winding space is when each half of the primary occupies about 30% of the space, and the secondary occupies 40%. Under this condition the figures given by Tables 9 and 10 have to be modified slightly. For maximum efficiency at mid-band, the turns for 1,000 ohms should be divided by 1.1, the maximum power in watts figure reduced by 1.2, and the mid-band losses increased by 1.2. The L.F. cut-off frequency will also be multiplied by 1.2.

## 200 Hz Cut-off Matching

With push-pull type outputs the author does not recommend the incorporation of 200 Hz cut-off in the output transformer. A preferable method is to incorporate the bass cut between the output transformer and the matching transformer by means of a series condenser, which should be chosen so that its reactance at the cut-off frequency is equal to the load impedance referred to that point.

## Methods of Winding and Connection

For the smaller size push-pull output transformers, the best method of winding to preserve a good balance at the higher frequencies is to wind one-half of the primary before, and the other half after, the secondary. The two ends of these two windings which are adjacent to the secondary are then connected together to form the centre tap. This method is shown diagrammatically at Fig. 21a.

For larger sizes, and especially those intended for Q.P.P. type output circuits, closer coupling of the windings may be considered necessary. The method of winding and connection shown at Fig. 21b has been proved to give very accurate balance indeed at the high frequencies. Some authorities recommend

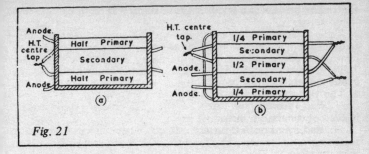

*Fig. 21*

complicated arrangements using a divided bobbin, so as to maintain geometrical symmetry. The arrangement here shown maintains just as good electrical symmetry, with a far simpler winding arrangement, and gives a wider frequency response band for a given size and complexity of design. The secondaries are shown as two windings connected in parallel. This arrangement preserves the best balance, especially if the secondary has a fairly high impedance. If the secondary impedance is quite low compared to the primary, then a series arrangement will serve equally well, when the junction can be used as a centre tap, and earthed.

For loudspeaker matching transformers, a simple arrangement with the primary and secondary (each in only one section) is adequate. It is not important in this case which winding is nearest to the core, so the order of winding may be determined by convenience from the point of view of the particular wire gauges to be used.

*Example 20*

A push-pull amplifier giving an output of 10 watts, with an anode to anode load of 4,000 ohms, requires an output transformer with an efficiency of about 90% to match it to a 10 ohm speaker for music and speech.

A 1″ stack of 1″ waste-free laminations operating at maximum mid-band efficiency has 8.5% losses and a cut-off of 65 Hz. If the turns are multiplied by 1.25, then the mid-band losses become $1.1 \times 8.5 = 9.5\%$ (or an efficiency of 90.5%), and the cut-off becomes $65 \div 1.5 = 43$ Hz. Thus the maximum output at 50 Hz can now be $1.5 \times 7 = 10.5$ watts. The winding for 4,000 ohms will require a total of

$$\sqrt{\frac{4,000}{1,000}} \times 960 \text{ or } 1920 \text{ turns.}$$

The turns for a 1,000 ohm winding will need to be $1.25 \times 770 =$

960. The turns, and a winding for 10 ohms will require

$$\sqrt{\frac{10}{1,000}} \times 960 = 96 \text{ turns.}$$

Thus the winding will be:

1. Half Primary, 960 turns.
2. Secondary, 96 turns.
3. Half Primary, 960 turns.

*Example 21*

A large amplifier, having an output of 40 watts, has an anode to anode load figure of 8,000 ohms, and requires to be matched to 250 ohms for speaker distribution. Give appropriate designs in standard transformer iron and in Radiometal, for use on music and speech, efficiency to be 95%.

Using standard transformer iron: Either a 2½" stack of 1¼" waste-free, or a 1½" stack of 1½" waste-free will satisfy the required conditions without modification. Each gives an efficiency of 95.2%.

Using Radiometal: A 1" stack of 1" waste-free gives a mid-band loss of 8.5 ÷ 1.7 = 5%. Under this condition the cut-off frequency is 65Hz, and maximum output without distortion would only be 7 x 2.3 = 16 watts. A 1½" stack of 1" waste-free gives, under maximum mid-band efficiency, a loss of 7.4 ÷ 1.7 = 4.35%, a cut-off of 60 Hz, and a maximum output of 12 x 2.3 = 27.6 watts. Increasing the turns by 1.25, the maximum power is increased to 1.5 x 27.6 = 41 watts, the mid-band losses become 4.35 x 1.1 = 4.8%, and the L.F. cut-off will be 60 ÷ 1.5 = 40 Hz.

Thus it is seen that a 1½" stack of 1" waste-free Radiometal will give almost identical performance with that of either a 2½" stack of 1¼", or a 1½" stack of 1½" in standard transformer iron. This results in a reduction of outside dimensions from 3¾" x 4½" to 2½" x 3".

To complete the design in Radiometal: The turns for a 1,000 ohm winding will be 670 ÷ 1.3 x 1.25 = 640 approx. Thus the primary will require a total of

$$640 \times \sqrt{\frac{8,000}{1,000}} = 1,800 \text{ turns}$$

and the secondary turns will be

74

$$640 \times \sqrt{\frac{250}{1,000}} = 320.$$

Thus, following the winding arrangement of Fig. 21b, the required sections are: 1. Quarter Primary, 450 turns; 2. Secondary, 320 turns; 3, Half Primary, 900 turns; 4. Secondary, 320 turns; 5. Quarter Primary, 450 turns.

*Example 22*

A cabinet type speaker with a speech coil impedance of 15 ohms is required to take one-eighth of the power from Example 21. Efficiency to be not less than 80%.

One-eighth of the power is 40/8 = 5 watts. The primary impedance must be 8 x 250 = 2,000 ohms. Using a ¾" stack of ¾" waste-free, with 1.75 times the turns from Table 9, the maximum power is 3 x 1.75 = 5.25, the mid-band losses are 1.7 x 11.25 = 19.5%, and a L.F. cut-off of 90 ÷ 3 = 30 Hz. This satisfies the conditions. Then the turns required are:—

1. Primary $750 \times 1.75 \times \sqrt{\dfrac{2,000}{1,000}} = 1,850$ turns.

2. Secondary $750 \times 1.75 \times \sqrt{\dfrac{15}{1,000}} = 160$ turns.

*Example 23*

A horn type speaker, speech coil impedance 5 ohms, is required to take one-quarter of the power from the same amplifier, with a 200 Hz bass-cut. What condenser is required, and what will be the efficiency, using the same size transformer as Example 22.

Using maximum mid-band efficiency, this size can handle 28 watts at 200 Hz, with losses of 11.5%, giving an efficiency of 88.5%. The primary impedance will be 4 x 250 or 1,000 ohms. Thus the condenser must have an impedance of 1,000 ohms at 200 Hz:

$$C = \frac{1,000,000}{2 \times 3.14 \times 200 \times 1,000} = 0.8 \ \mu F.$$

Turns required as follows:—

1. Primary, 750 turns.

2. Secondary, $750 \times \sqrt{\dfrac{5}{1,000}} = 53$ מגודל

## Chapter 11

## INPUT AND INTER-VALVE TRANSFORMERS
## (PARALLEL FED)

### Core Material

It is essential for good reproduction of the low frequencies at low levels to have a material for the core which will maintain the inductance at very small values of A.C. magnetization. Ordinary transformer iron has a low initial permeability. Mumetal is the best material at present produced from this viewpoint. It has a higher permeability than other materials, but saturation occurs at a lower value, and hence it is not suitable where power is required.

The best shape for this type of transformer is shown in Fig. 22, together with full dimensions. Another type, having much larger winding window, has had considerable favour, but it will be realised that increasing the cross section of iron will reduce the turns necessary for any given impedance. For this reason the shape shown gives not only a wider frequency band, but also gives a more level response within that range, by reducing tendencies to L.F. and H.F. resonances. The core stack should be 7/16th", so that the section is square.

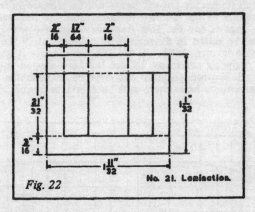

*Fig. 22*　　　　　　　No. 21. Lamination.

### Turns and Ratio

If the valve into which the transformer operates is a triode, a secondary composed of 4,000 turns of 44 S.W.G. enamelled copper wire will give as good a step-up condition as any smaller

77

gauge. But if the valve following the transformer is a tetrode or pentode the input capacity will be much smaller, and so further advantage can be gained by reducing the wire gauge, so that the secondary may consist of 6,000 turns of 46 S.W.G. enamelled copper wire.

Fig. 23 shows the form of frequency response when the primary impedance referred to the secondary is 65,000 ohms in the case of the 4,000 turn winding, or 150,000 ohms in the case of the 6,000 turn winding. (These curves allow for a valve input capacity, including strays, but not that of the transformer winding, of 100–120 pF in the first case, and 30–50 pF in the second case.) At the low frequency end, curve A is for input transformers, or inter-valve transformers, where the coupling capacity is considerably greater than the value given for curve B. Curve B is for an inter-valve transformer in which the coupling capacity is $N^2 \times 0.16$ $\mu$F., where N is the transformer step-up ratio. If the value of coupling condenser is smaller than this, there will be a tendency to produce an L.F. resonance in the region of cut-off, which will need to be damped by the method shown later in this section, unless for some reason the resonance should be desirable.

The step-up may be increased by reducing the primary turns, which will increase the impedance referred to the secondary in proportion to the square of the increase in turns ratio. This will result in narrowing the frequency band from both ends. The whole high frequency cut-off curve will be reduced in frequency by the square of the increase in turns ratio. In the cases where curve A applies for the low frequency end, the whole cut-off curve will be raised in frequency by approximately the cube of the increase in turns ratio. In the case where curve B applies, the value of coupling condenser to give the same shaped cut-off be reduced in proportion to the cube of the increase in turns ratio, when the whole curve will be raised in frequency by the

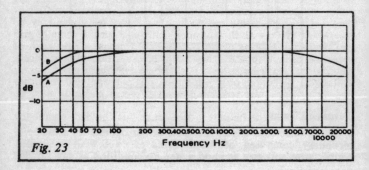

*Fig. 23*

78

same ratio. These statements are only approximate. Mumetal has the peculiarity that the inductance of any given number of turns using a Mumetal core is reasonably constant below 50 Hz, but above that frequency gradually tends to vary inversely proportional to frequency, so that above about 600 Hz the law is such that the inductance has a constant reactance. Thus if the ratio is increased so that the cut-off begins above 600 Hz, then the effect will change from that of increasing the cut-off, to one of introducing further loss over the entire frequency. Otherwise stated further increase in step-up ratio will not result in further increased true step-up.

## Primary Impedance

In the case of input transformers, the primary impedance is simply that of the device for which the input is matched — microphone, pick-up, etc. In the case of an inter-valve transformer, the primary impedance may be taken as the equivalent parallel resistance of the preceding valve anode impedance and its anode coupling resistance.

## Resonances

It is possible for a peak in the frequency response to appear due to resonance in the region of either the low frequency cut-off, the high frequency cut-off, or both. If the size recommended is used, the possibility of an H.F. resonance is greatly reduced, but use of a small value of coupling condenser may introduce an L.F. resonance. With the older shaped core, necessitating many more turns for the same impedance, both types of resonance were more likely to appear.

With both types of resonance, the peak may be reduced either by increasing the primary impedance or by introducing a secondary shunt resistance in the form of a grid leak. The primary impedance can usually be increased enough merely by raising the value of anode resistance. If this cannot produce sufficient damping without going to too high a value, a resistance may be inserted in series with the coupling condenser, or the value of grid leak adjusted to bring about the desired response. With each of these methods, response at both ends of the scale will be reduced, so that they may be applied if there are two resonances, one at each end. If there is only a resonance at one end, and the other end does not require reduction, then different methods must be applied.

If there is a low frequency resonance but the high frequency cut-off does not need reduction, then a resistance connected across the primary of the transformer (after the coupling condenser, not from anode to earth), will reduce the resonance at the low frequency end, and at the same time have the effect of improving the high frequency response.

If there is a high frequency peak, but the low frequency response has none, then a resistance connected in series with the grid will reduce the high frequency peak without introducing greater loss at the low frequency end.

*Example 24*

An input transformer is required to give the maximum step-up for speech only (200 Hz cut-off) to work into a pentode grid. Find the step-up that can be used from a microphone of 600 ohms impedance.

From the A curve, the 3 dB point is seen to be just above 30 Hz. This means that the cut-off can be multiplied by about 6.4 to bring it to 200 Hz. From tables the cube root of 6.4 is found to be about 1.85 and the square of 1.85 is about 3.4. Then the referred impedance can be about 3.4 x 150,000 ohms, or 500,000 ohms. The impedance step-up can be 500,000/600, or nearly 900/1. This gives a turns ratio of $\sqrt{900}$, or 30/1. So the windings on the Transformer will be:—

1. Secondary, 6,000 turns.
2. Primary, 200 turns.

*Example 25*

A triode having an anode impedance of 2,500 ohms is used with an anode coupling resistance of 10,000 ohms. What step-up can be used to give the response of Fig. 23 with a secondary of 4,000 turns of 44E, and what coupling condenser should be used?

The primary impedance is the effective impedance of 2,500 and 10,000 ohms in parallel or

$$\frac{2,500 \times 10,000}{2,500 + 10,000} = 2,000 \text{ ohms.}$$

This is to be referred to the secondary as 65,000 ohms, so the impedance ratio of the transformer is 65,000/2,000, or just over 30/1. This gives a turns ratio of just over 5.5/1. The secondary turns are 4,000, so an appropriate primary will be about 700 turns. To give the response of curve B in Fig. 23, the coupling condenser should be 30 x 0.16, or 5 $\mu$F. Probably a 4 $\mu$F, being a standard value, will be adequate. However, this value may be too large to be practical, in which case a smaller one, say 0.5 $\mu$F, may be used. A resistance of about 20,000 ohms across the primary will damp the resonance, and the cut-off will now be at about 50 Hz.

## Chapter 12

# PUSH-PULL INTER-VALVE TRANSFORMERS

When an inter-valve transformer has to provide signal for the grids of two valves in push-pull, it is essential that each valve should receive its signal identical in amplitude and in opposite phase to the other. For the lower and middle frequencies, accurate division of turns will secure this condition, but for the upper frequencies further precaution must be taken to maintain this balance.

A simple method enabling an ordinary inter-valve with only one secondary to be used, is that of connecting two equal resistances across the secondary in series, and taking the centre tap of these resistances to earth or grid bias. Then each end of the secondary is connected to one grid. This method suffers from the disadvantage that the capacity between each end of the secondary winding and earth is not equal, and so these two equal high resistances may be regarded as being shunted by unequal capacities, which, of course, upsets the balance at the high frequency end.

The better method is to wind two separate secondaries so that they are equally well coupled to the primary, and have as near as possible the same capacity from their "live" end to earth. On the size detailed in the previous section, this may be achieved by winding one secondary of 3,000 turns before the primary, and then the other secondary of 3,000 turns after the primary. The difference in winding capacity will not be great, and will in practice be much smaller than the input capacity of the valves, which will thus help to reduce the effective inequality. The two ends of the secondaries adjacent to the primary should be connected together to form the centre tap, while the extreme ends go to the grids.

As each grid is now only across one-half as many turns, and the turns are rather better coupled to the primary, the input capacity per grid may be rather more than twice the figure given in Chapter 11 to obtain the same high frequency characteristic — i.e., about 70–120 pF. Thus, the ratio may be calculated by making the impedance ratio from primary to the whole secondary such that the primary impedance is stepped up to about 150,000 ohms.

If push-pull feed back is being used, or separate grid returns for bias purposes, the two "inside" ends of the secondary may be brought out separately for the purpose.

In designing push-pull transformers of this size, it is necessary to make sure that a certain voltage limit is not exceeded, otherwise distortion will be quickly introduced. A safe figure may be taken as 80 turns per volt at 50 Hz. This means that the total voltage across 6,000 turns should not exceed 75. If negative feedback is being used, do not forget to add the feedback voltage to the grid voltage, as this will be the total voltage required across the transformer secondaries.

If this voltage limit is going to be exceeded, then a larger size is necessary. If possible, a lamination size similar in shape to that of Fig. 22, but larger, should be chosen, and all the details multiplied up proportionately. The safe turns per volt will decrease as the cross-sectional area of the core increases. Thus, if a $\frac{3}{8}''$ stack of a size having a centre limb width of $\frac{3}{8}''$ is used, the area is $\frac{3}{8}'' \times \frac{3}{8}''$ instead of 7/16th" x 7/16th" or about double. Therefore the safe turns per volt is reduced to about half, or 40. If 6,000 turns were still used for the secondary, the safe voltage at 50 Hz would be $6,000/40 = 150$ – twice the previous figure. At present the author knows of only one lamination manufacturer who has tools for such a size, and to date this size has not been produced in Mumetal. A similar overall size is obtained by use of the lamination shown in Fig. 24, which is supplied in Mumetal.

On this shape, the safe turns per volt are the same as with the smaller size, because the cross-section of the centre limb is the same. So higher voltage can only be accommodated by increasing the turns. Multiplication by 1.4 to 8,500, and using the same referred impedance, with a divided secondary, will give approximately the same results as those shown in Fig. 23. This gives a safe grid-to-grid voltage at 50 Hz of 105. If step-up is increased beyond this point by simply increasing the secondary turns

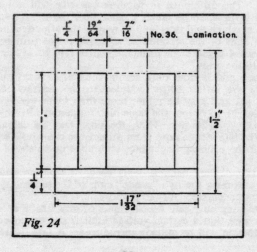

Fig. 24

(thereby increasing the ratio), the cut-off at the top end of the scale will fall in the same way as shown for a corresponding increase in ratio in Chapter 11, but the L.F. cut-off will remain unchanged. If the safe voltage is increased by increasing primary and secondary turns proportionately (thereby maintaining the same ratio), then the low frequency cut-off will be reduced to a lower frequency, and the high frequency cut-off will be reduced by a less amount, but it will progressively begin to show signs of peaking. This peak can be reduced by the methods outlined in Chapter 11.

# Chapter 13

## CONSTRUCTION DETAILS

### Preparing a Bobbin

Unless a bobbin of the correct size is available ready-made, it will be necessary to fabricate one. Details are given here of two types that are simple to construct without special tools.

Fig. 25 illustrates the method with the first type, which is suited for the smaller sizes, as it gives adequate strength to support a small winding, whilst taking up little of the available winding space. It should be constructed from stiff cartridge paper, or similar material. Five pieces should be cut, according to the final required dimensions, one as at (a), and two each as at (b) and (c). A centre block, as at (d) will be required to support the bobbin while winding, and may also be used in making up the bobbin. Great care should be taken in the construction of this centre block, to ensure that all its faces are "square", and to

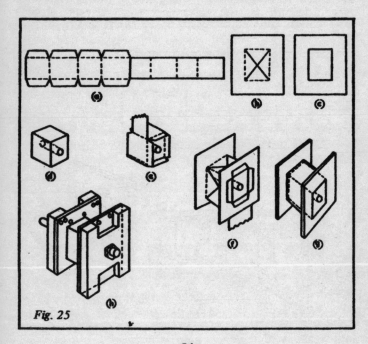

*Fig. 25*

the correct dimensions (very slightly larger than the core cross-section, and a little shorter than the window length, about 1/64th"). Also, to see that the hole drilled through it is absolutely parallel to its sides. The method of bending each of the parts is clearly shown in sketches (e), (f) and (g) of Fig. 25. At each stage the parts of the bobbin should be carefully glued so that the whole bobbin is united by glue, but is not stuck to the centre block, as this has to be removed after winding. After the glue has set, small holes may be drilled or punched in the cheeks of the bobbin, so that the winding leads may be brought out and properly anchored. Finally, end support plates will be needed during winding. These should be made of metal or wood, and secured in position by the centre spindle as shown at (h). The holes drilled in both the centre block and the end support plates should be only just the required clearance hole for the size of centre spindle to be used – say, 2 B.A. Nuts on the centre spindle are used to secure the whole assembly, and should be tight enough to secure that the spindle will not turn by itself inside.

Fig. 26 shows a method of construction for larger bobbins, where the fabricated bobbin would not be strong enough to support the winding. It is made of bakelized paper or cloth sheet, about 1/16th" thick. It has the advantage that all the parts

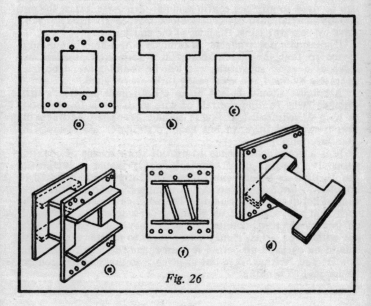

*Fig. 26*

can be cut from sheet – no tube is required – and that the "tags" on two of the centre-pieces prevent the cheeks from falling off during or after winding. Two pieces each are required as sketched at (a), (b) and (c). Necessary holes in the cheeks for lead-outs and anchoring may be made before the bobbin is assembled. The method of assembly is clearly shown by sketches (d), (e) and (f). A centre block and end support plates will be required, to mount up for winding. The centre block will be exactly the same in form as that shown at Fig. 25 (d), but the end support plates must be different, being only simple rectangular pieces with a hole in the middle, of such dimensions that they fit conveniently between the end "tags" of the centre-pieces. A spindle will again be required, but for the larger sizes should not be relied upon to turn the bobbin during winding. It is suggested that one or two additional small holes be made in the end plates and centre block, through which steel pins should be inserted to provide means of obtaining a positive drive to the bobbin.

## Improvising a Winding Machine

Two fundamental arrangements are necessary for successful winding: a means of rotating the bobbin, and some provision for holding the reel of wire. A lathe makes a very successful winding machine. For the smaller sizes a standard three or four jaw chuck can be used to grip the centre spindle. For larger sizes, the pins already inserted into the centre block may be arranged to take a drive by bearing against the jaws of the chuck.

If a lathe is not available, an ordinary wheel-brace mounted in a vice so that the chuck rotates in a horizontal position, will serve as a good substitute. It will be found rather laborious, operating by hand, if a great many turns are required.

A spindle should be set up in a horizontal position a little distance away to hold the reel of wire so that it is free to rotate as wire is required. The wire should be passed between the thumb and first finger of one hand to steady it and to apply the necessary tension.

It is a great convenience to provide some means of counting turns. If a proper turns counter is not available, a cyclometer can be used as a good substitute. The turns counter should be coupled to the machine so that it numbers upwards in the direction of rotation when winding. The winding direction should be such that the wire goes on to the upper side of the bobbin. If an improvised turns counter is used, it may not register coincident with turns – i.e., it may take 5 turns to register each 1. This should be checked up before it is used, and the required readings at start and finish worked out in advance so that all attention can be devoted to winding.

## Methods of Winding

Wire gauges of, say, 24 and larger may be brought out of the bobbin direct, and a length wound around either the centre spindle or some convenient peg to keep it out of the way while winding, until it can be terminated after winding is complete.

Wire gauges of, say, 26 and smaller should be carefully joined by soldering to a piece of silk-covered flex, taking care that a neat, flat joint is made that will not take up too much room, and will not cut through and cause short-circuited turns. It should be insulated at the joint by means of a small piece of insulating material. The silk flex should come out through the hole in the bobbin, and should make about two turns round the bobbin before the proper wire gauge "takes over". The silk flex should be anchored conveniently to await proper termination after winding.

All windings should be wound so that one turn lays as close as possible to its neighbour, until a layer is full, when another layer should be commenced in the return direction. On larger size coils, a layer of paper insulation will be inserted between every layer, or perhaps every few layers, to prevent a turn from a high layer from slipping down into contact with lower layers. On smaller coils, and particularly with the very small gauges (beyond, say 36), it is not possible to insulate the layers in this way, and a method known as "random" winding is employed. The turns still go on approximately in layers, but it is not possible to guarantee that no space is lost between adjacent turns of the same layer, and so later turns may fill spaces left previously. In winding by this method care should be taken that the winding builds up level along the whole width of the bobbin, otherwise useful winding space will be wasted. For this reason it is especially important, too, that the bobbin shall rotate "true". This means that when the centre is spun before winding is commenced, the four sides of the centre must turn parallel with the spindle, and not show any sign of a skew wobble, and further the cheeks must not show any sign of wobble from side to side.

At the finish of the winding, the end should be brought out in the same way as the beginning was, according to the gauge being used.

## Insulation

Between windings, as well as between the layers on larger sizes, a layer or two of insulation must be provided. Two or three layers of very thin material are better than one layer of thicker material. This should be cut to the exact width between the bobbin cheeks, and wound on carefully and tightly over the winding. The insulation may be of thin high-quality paper, or may be of one of the acetate substitutes. Before proceeding with a further winding, the insulation should be firmly secured in position by the use of a little adhesive. For paper, some Chatterton's compound, or, as an alternative, some high-quality wax, may be used to fix the last turn of the paper to the preceding one by applying quickly after heating momentarily on the butt of a soldering iron. If one of the acetate films is used, a little acetate may be quickly applied to weld the film, but care must be taken to see that no acetate comes into contact with the wire if it is enamel insulated, as the acetate may dissolve or soften the enamel and cause turns to short.

## Terminating the Windings

After winding is complete, a layer of insulation should be wound on to cover the windings and insulate them from possible contact with the outside limb of the laminations. Then all the ends of windings should be properly terminated. The ends should each be threaded through the pairs of holes in one of the corners of the bobbin several times. Before so threading, the whole length that will go through the holes should be stripped of insulation. The threading should allow the portion of lead from the hole where it comes out of the bobbin to the corner where it is threaded to lie slack. If it is tight, it may break later, especially if the bobbin cheek is slightly flexible and may bend. After threading in this way, the end should be quickly tinned with a soldering iron, which will secure it, and also provide a form of tag to which the external leads can be soldered.

## Laminating and Finishing

Care must be taken when inserting the laminations that they do not damage the winding. For a choke, or a transformer in which there is D.C. flowing, all the E-shaped pieces, or T-shaped pieces, should be inserted first from the same side, until the centre of the bobbin is full of laminations. An equal stack of I- or U-shaped pieces should then be taken, and brought into contact with the E's or T's with the appropriate gap spacing. Some form of clamps will be necessary to hold the whole core together and keep the gap tight up to the spacing used. These can easily be improvised, using an appropriate width of strip metal which can be drilled for clamping bolts either side of the laminations, and possibly the end of the clamps can be turned over to form mounting feet for the completed component.

For transformers with no D.C. the laminations of different shapes should be inserted from opposite sides of the bobbin in pairs. A convenient way of doing this quickly is to arrange a small stack of each shape on each side of the bobbin. Then, by working with both hands, alternate pairs may be picked up and inserted quite quickly. When laminating is complete, similar clamping arrangements to those suggested for the choke may be employed.

Ordinary transformer iron is very subject to attack by rust, so it is a good plan, when the component is complete, to paint the exposed edges of the core with a good quality paint as a protection against rust.

The clamps may be bent at one end to provide feet for mounting, and at the other end to take a bakelized sheet panel on which soldering tags or terminals are mounted to make a finished terminal board for the transformer or choke.

# Chapter 14

## METHODS OF TESTING

### Turns Ratio

This is comparatively simple to check, if there is available A.C. mains, two A.C. voltmeters, and a variety of odd resistances. At least one of the voltmeters should be a high-grade multi-range instrument. The other may be any indicating instrument that will give a consistent indication when the same volts are applied. In this case, readings on the poorer instrument may be calibrated by comparing the two instruments in parallel on the same voltage, adjusting the voltage to various values by means of different arrangements of resistances.

It is important when checking turns ratio that an A.C. voltage no higher than that for which any given winding is designed shall be used. Having checked on this by calculation, readings can be taken of the voltage across the two windings, first by feeding a voltage into the primary and measuring the voltage on both primary and secondary simultaneously with the aid of both voltmeters, then by feeding a voltage into the secondary. The ratios of these two sets of readings can then be calculated, and if there is any discrepancy between them, the mean value may be taken as the correct one.

### Frequency Response

This requires more apparatus than the previous test. An audio oscillator is needed, together with some voltmeters whose performance at various frequencies besides 50 Hz is reliable. Also, the conditions under which the component is to operate must be simulated. That is, the primary must have the signal applied to it from an impedance equal to the one which it will have in practice, and the secondary must work into the same impedance as that for which it is intended. If it is designed to operate with D.C. flowing in one winding, then this condition, too, must be reproduced in testing its response.

### Transformers with no D.C. Components

Fig. 27 shows a way in which components of the types detailed in Chapter 5 may be tested. The resistance between the primary voltmeter and the actual primary is equal to the equivalent source impedance. In the case of a push-pull output transformer (class A) it will be twice the anode impedance of each valve. The resistance across the secondary is equal to the required

90

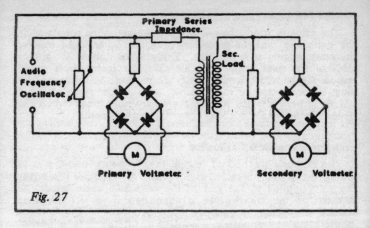

*Fig. 27*

load impedance at the secondary. It should be noted that the primary source impedance is not the same as the optimum load at the primary side. It may be more (as in the case of transformer to work with tetrodes or pentodes) or less (as in the case of transformer to work with triodes).

A frequency response may be taken by setting the voltage at the primary voltmeter to the same reading, and then noting the reading on the secondary voltmeter. If the readings on the secondary voltmeter are plotted against frequency on graph paper, a frequency response will be obtained.

In the case of loudspeaker transformers, the source impedance should be that of the output valve, as it will be referred to the primary of this transformer.

### Example 26

An amplifier has output valves having an anode impedance of 2,500 ohms each, and an optimum load of 8,000 ohms anode to anode. This is matched to 250 ohms. From this it is distributed to several speakers. One of these is intended to take one-eighth of the output.

The output transformer has a step-down of 8,000/250 or 32/1 impedance ratio. Thus, the source impedance at the secondary will be 2,500/32 = 78 ohms. The share of this applicable to a speaker taking one-eighth of the power will be 8 x 78, or 625 ohms, while the load impedance referred to this primary, due to its own speaker load on the secondary, will be 8 x 250, or 2,000 ohms.

## Parallel Fed Inter-Valve Transformers

The primary source impedance for these may be simulated in the same way, but the secondary must also be arranged to have the same loading as in practice. This may be only at the grid or grids of the next stage. In this case, the meter itself would impose a load which would falsify the reading. So the secondary must be connected to valve grid, or grids, in the same way as it will be in practice, and the signal voltage in the anode circuit can be read by resistance capacity coupling to a voltmeter.

## Transformers with D.C. Flowing

The simplest method of testing the frequency response is to set up the actual operating conditions. A voltmeter measuring the volts applied to the grid of the valve into whose anode the primary of the transformer is connected is set to the same reading at different frequencies. The secondary reading is taken in the same way as before, according to whether it is an output or inter-valve transformer.

## Air Gap Adjustment of Chokes and Transformers carrying D.C.

A simple method of doing this is to set up a full-wave rectifier circuit with no smoothing. Across this, connect the component to be tested in series with a resistance to limit the D.C. to its rated value. If, on measuring the A.C. component across the choke, this is more than required in practice, a suitable reservoir condenser should be applied across the supply to reduce it to a practical value. Check that the D.C. flowing is correct, as altering the reservoir condenser alters the output of a rectifier. Having ascertained that D.C. flowing and A.C. across are correct, connect the A.C. voltmeter in series with a D.C. blocking condenser across the resistance in series with the choke, and adjust the gap. The highest inductance will be when the voltmeter across the resistance shows the lowest reading.

## Winding Insulation

The insulation between windings and between each winding and earth should be tested with a suitable "flash test" device. This is simply a fairly high voltage (higher than that which the insulation must stand in practice), either A.C. or D.C. In series with the supply on one side is a high resistance, sufficient to limit a short-circuit current to about 5 mA, and a neon bulb. The other side is connected to an earth plate on which the component can be placed for test. To the high potential side is connected an insulated test prod. The usual procedure for a transformer would be as follows: Earth secondary with a lead and apply test prod to primary; earth primary with lead and apply test prod to secondary. The neon should not light in either case. Finally, to check the tester connection, the prod may touch the earth plate, when the neon should light.

In the case of a choke, of course, the component is simply placed on the earth plate and the prod applied to the winding terminals.

## Shorted Turns Tester

A useful adjunct to the regular winder is some device to detect the existence of shorted turns before the component is cored up, thus saving time if the component should prove faulty.

A simple method of constructing such an instrument is to make up a simple triode feed-back oscillator of any type (to give, say, 400 Hz), using for the coil an inductance, wound on an iron core of similar or slightly smaller cross-section to the components to be tested. Instead of making this inductance in the usual way of an iron-cored inductance, it is so arranged that the core is open and can have the coil to be tested placed over the core adjacent to the inductance coil of the oscillator, which is arranged so that it can be adjusted by means of a variable bias control, so that it only just operates. Under this condition, if the coil applied for test has any shorted turns, then the oscillation will either stop, or be greatly reduced in amplitude. On the other hand, self-capacity in the coil applied will only alter the frequency slightly.

# Chapter 15

# CALCULATION OF WIRE GAUGE

Table 11 in this section enables the correct wire gauge to be chosen to get a given number of turns into a given winding space. For each wire gauge, with its covering there appears two figures: the figure for turns per inch should be used for cases of layer winding, and the figure for turns per square inch for random winding. To illustrate the use of these tables, the wire gauges for each example given in the previous Chapters is worked out below.

*Example 27*
The winding area in this case (see Fig. 12) is 0.275 sq. in. It is required to get 6,300 turns into this space. This is equivalent to 6,300/0.275 = 23,000 turns per sq. in. 38 S.W.G. enamelled only gives 21,000 turns per sq. in., so the next even gauge will be 40 S.W.G.

*Example 28*
This is on the same size, but as the turns are fairly low, it should be possible to layer-wind it. Using 32 S.W.G. enamelled gives 83 turns per inch, or just over 50 in a ⅝" layer. This requires 1,650/50 = 33 layers. At 83 turns per inch 33 layers will occupy a depth of 33/83 = 0.39". If the paper used is 0.003" thick, 33 layers will take up 0.1", total 0.49". This allows enough for top insulation to make up ½".

*Example 29*
Using the figure from Table 3, the winding space will be about ⅞" × ⅜", or 0.33 sq. in. The turns will be 6,300 × 3.2 = 20,000 turns. This requires 20,000/0.33 = 60,000 per sq. in. 44 S.W.G. enamelled gives 65,000 per sq. in.

*Example 30*
900 turns will again be layer-wound. Using 22 S.W.G. enamelled gives 33 turns per inch, or 70 per 2⅛" layer. 900 turns at 70 per layer requires 13 layers, say 14, as there will be very little clearance. 14 layers at 33 turns per inch will take up 14/33 = 0.43". Allowing for layer insulation will bring this to about 0.48". This leaves a good tolerance, but it will probably be needed with a fairly heavy wire gauge and a long-shaped bobbin.

*Example 31*
In this case there are two windings, one of 2,400 and one of 12,000, to be wound in a space of 0.86 sq. in. 40 S.W.G. enamelled gives 31,500 turns per sq. in. Thus, 12,000 takes about 0.4

Table 11. S.W.G. Turns per inch and Turns per sq inch

| S.W.G. | Enamel covered | | Enamel and single silk covered | | Single silk covered | | Double silk covered | | Single cotton covered | | Double cotton covered | |
|---|---|---|---|---|---|---|---|---|---|---|---|---|
| | Turns per inch | Turns per sq inch | Turns per inch | Turns per sq inch | Turns per inch | Turns per sq inch | Turns per inch | Turns per sq inch | Turns per inch | Turns per sq inch | Turns per inch | Turns per sq inch |
| 16 | 14.8 | 219 | 14 | 196 | 14.8 | 219 | 14.4 | 207 | 13.8 | 190 | 13 | 169 |
| 18 | 19.6 | 383 | 18.9 | 357 | 19.8 | 392 | 19.4 | 376 | 18 | 324 | 16.8 | 282 |
| 20 | 26 | 675 | 24.5 | 600 | 26 | 675 | 25.2 | 635 | 23.5 | 550 | 21 | 441 |
| 22 | 33 | 1090 | 31 | 960 | 33 | 1090 | 31.8 | 1010 | 29.2 | 850 | 25.3 | 640 |
| 24 | 41.5 | 1720 | 38.5 | 1550 | 42 | 1760 | 37 | 1370 | 36.5 | 1330 | 31 | 960 |
| 26 | 50 | 2500 | 48 | 2300 | 50.5 | 2550 | 48 | 2300 | 43 | 1850 | 35 | 1225 |
| 28 | 61 | 3700 | 57 | 3250 | 61 | 3700 | 57 | 3250 | 50.5 | 2550 | 39 | 1520 |
| 30 | 73 | 5300 | 67 | 4500 | 72 | 5200 | 66.5 | 4400 | 57 | 3250 | 44.5 | 1980 |
| 32 | 83 | 6900 | 76 | 5800 | 82 | 6700 | 74 | 5500 | 63 | 4000 | 48 | 2300 |
| 34 | 97 | 9400 | 88 | 7750 | 94 | 8850 | 84 | 7050 | 69 | 4760 | 51.5 | 2650 |
| 36 | 116 | 13400 | 102 | 10400 | 112 | 12500 | 97 | 9400 | 85 | 7200 | 59.5 | 3550 |
| 38 | 145 | 21000 | 125 | 15600 | 135 | 18200 | 113 | 12700 | 98 | 9600 | 67 | 4500 |
| 40 | 178 | 31500 | 151 | 22700 | 160 | 25600 | 132 | 17400 | 112 | 12500 | 76 | 5800 |
| 42 | 208 | 43000 | 175 | 30500 | 188 | 35400 | 158 | 25000 | — | — | — | — |
| 44 | 255 | 71000 | 208 | 43000 | 222 | 49000 | 182 | 33000 | — | — | — | — |
| 46 | 330 | 110000 | 255 | 71000 | 270 | 75000 | 212 | 45000 | — | — | — | — |

sq. in. For the primary, 34 S.W.G. enamelled gives 9,400 turns per sq. in., so 2,400 turns takes up 2,400/9,400 = 0.266". Total area, 0.666". This allows good margin for insulation.

*Example 32*

In this case the two windings have to occupy 0.56 sq. in. 12,000 turns, as before, take 0.4 sq. in. in 40 S.W.G. enamelled. Using 42 S.W.G. enamelled, 43,000 turns per sq. in., 12,000 turns take 12,000/43,000 = 0.28 sq. in. 4,000 turns of 40 S.W.G. enamelled take 0.135 sq. in., total 0.415 sq. in.

*Example 33*

Here, again, layer-winding will be used. For the 3,800 turns, using 36 S.W.G. enamelled, 116 turns per inch gives about 156 per layer (1⅜"). This requires 3,800/156 = 25 layers. 25 layers will take 25/116 = 0.216" for wire, and at 0.003" per layer insulation, 0.075", total 0.291". For the 220 turns, using 20 S.W.G. enamelled, 26 turns per inch gives 35 per layer. This will require 7 layers, taking up 7/26 = 0.27" for wire, and 0.021" for insulation, total 0.291". Total depth of both windings 0.582", which leaves room for insulation between windings and on top in a bobbin of depth ⅝" or 0.625".

*Example 34*

Using the size from Table 2. Layer length ⅝", depth ½". Using 36 S.W.G. enamelled for 1,850 turns: 116 x⅝" or, say, 70 turns per layer, gives 1,850/70 = 27 layers. Wire 27/116 = 0.233", insulation 0.081", total 0.314". Using 22 S.W.G. enamelled for 74 turns. 33 x ⅝" or 20 turns per layer, gives 4 layers. Wire 4/33 = 0.122", insulation 0.12", total 0.134". Total winding depth 0.448" which allows room for insulation between and on top of the windings.

*Example 35*

A 1" waste-free will allow a layer length of 1⅜", and a total depth of 7/16th". Using 34 S.W.G. enamelled for primary windings. Turns per layer, 1⅜" x 97 — say, 130. Each half primary takes 960/130 or 8 layers (always take next whole number). Depth for wire 8/97 = 0.083", for insulation 0.024", total per half 0.107", for whole primary 0.214". Using 20 S.W.G. enamelled for secondary, giving 35 turns per layer, requires 3 layers, taking 0.116" for wire, 0.009" for insulation, total 0.125". Total depth for windings 0.339". Using 3 layers of 0.003" each between windings and on top, gives 0.027", total 0.366", which allows about 1/16th" clearance on top.

*Example 36*

Each quarter primary will use 4 layers of 34 S.W.G. enamelled taking 0.054" (including insulation). The half primary 8 layers taking 0.107", total for primary 0.215". Using 30 S.W.G. for the secondaries. 4 layers taking 0.068", total secondary space 0.136", total winding depth 0.351". Inter-winding insulation, as before, 0.045", total 0.396".

*Example 37*

A ¾" waste-free will allow a layer length of 1", and a depth of 5/16th". Using 38 S.W.G. enamelled, 13 layers, with insulation 0.130". And for secondary, using 22 S.W.G. enamelled, 5 layers, with insulation 0.167". Total, 0.297".

*Example 38*

For the primary, using 32 S.W.G. enamelled requires 10 layers, taking, with insulation, 0.150". For the secondary, 2 layers of 20 S.W.G. enamelled will just fit in. This will take, with insulation, 0.083", or, if another layer is required for the last few turns, 0.125". Total, 0.275".

*Example 39*

Here the winding space may be taken as 9/16th" x 3/16th", or 0.105 sq. in. 6,000 turns of 46 S.W.G. enamelled will occupy 6,000/110,000 = 0.055 sq. in. Allowing that only about 70% of such a small space can be utilised — i.e., 0.7 x 0.105 = 0.073 sq. in. — this leaves 0.018 sq. in. for the primary. If 200 turns are to go in 0.018 sq. in., there would be 200/0.018 = 11,100 per sq. in. 36 S.W.G. enamelled gives 13,400 per sq. in.

*Example 40*

4,000 turns of 44 S.W.G. enamelled will occupy 4,000/71,000 or 0.057 sq. in. This leaves about 0.016 for the primary. If 700 turns go in 0.016 sq. in., there would be 700/0.016 = 4,400 per sq. in. 30 S.W.G. enamelled gives 5,300 per sq. in.

# Chapter 16

## TABLES

### Copper Wire Comparison Tables

This table presents the nominal diameter and resistance (to four significant figures) of bare copper wire in various wire gauges. The gauges used are the Brown and Sharpe Gauge (B & S, also known as the American Wire Gauge (A.W.G.), the Imperial Standard Wire Gauge (S.W.G.) and the Metric Gauge.

The data are given in both English and metric units, the latter being included for the benefit of overseas readers and Europeans who are not familiar with the other units. The diameter in the English units is expressed in mils, a mil being 1/1000 in.

The diameters and resistances given in the table are subject to normal manufacturing tolerances. A typical figure for the tolerance of the diameter is plus or minus 1 per cent or 0.1 mil (0.0025mm in metric units) which ever is the larger. The resistance would be within plus or minus 2 per cent at 20 degrees C but varies with temperature. The resistance changes approximately 0.4 per cent for each degree C change in temperature, increased temperature giving increased resistance.

In the B & S gauge, the ratio of the diameter of any gauge number to that of the next larger gauge number is constant and is 1.1229. The corresponding ratio of cross sectional area is 1.1229 squared, or about 1.2610.

This means that for each increase in gauge number, the resistance per unit length increases by approximately 25 per cent. It is found that an increase in gauge number by 3 gives approximately double the resistance per unit length.

In the S.W.G. the diameters of the gauge do not follow a simple rule but rather form a series of short arithmetical progressions. From 18 S.W.G. to 23 S.W.G., for example, the diameter decreases by 4 mils per number whereas from 23 S.W.G. to 26 S.W.G. it decreases by 2 mils per number. In the Metric gauge the gauge number is ten times the diameter of the wire expressed in millimetres. The normally available sizes form a similar series to that of the S.W.G. Half sizes in the B & S and S.W.G. gauges (and intermediate sizes in the Metric gauge) are available to special order if required.

This data is presented in such a form as to allow easy comparison of the different standards, permitting a near equivalent to be selected if coil winding data (for example) specifies a gauge which is not readily available. If 38 B & S were specified for a coil, it can be seen that either 42 S.W.G. or 1.0 Metric has approximately the same diameter and could therefore be substituted.

Table 12
Nominal diameter and resistance measured at 20°C (68°F)

| GAUGE | | | ENGLISH UNITS | | METRIC UNITS | |
|---|---|---|---|---|---|---|
| B & S | S.W.G. | Metric | Diam. mils | Ohms per 1,000 ft | Diam. mm | Ohms per Km |
| — | — | 45 | 177.2 | 0.3304 | 4.5 | 1.084 |
| — | 7 | — | 176 | 0.3348 | 4.470 | 1.098 |
| 6 | — | — | 162.0 | 0.3951 | 4.116 | 1.296 |
| — | 8 | — | 160 | 0.4051 | 4.064 | 1.329 |
| — | — | 40 | 157.5 | 0.4182 | 4.0 | 1.372 |
| 7 | — | — | 144.3 | 0.4982 | 3.666 | 1.635 |
| — | 9 | — | 144 | 0.5001 | 3.658 | 1.641 |
| — | — | 35 | 137.8 | 0.6128 | 3.5 | 1.792 |
| 8 | — | — | 128.5 | 0.6282 | 3.265 | 2.061 |
| — | 10 | — | 128 | 0.6330 | 3.251 | 2.077 |
| — | — | 30 | 118.1 | 0.7434 | 3.0 | 2.439 |
| — | 11 | — | 116 | 0.7707 | 2.946 | 2.529 |
| 9 | — | — | 114.4 | 0.7921 | 2.906 | 2.599 |
| — | — | 28 | 110.2 | 0.8534 | 2.8 | 2.800 |
| — | 12 | — | 104 | 0.9588 | 2.642 | 3.146 |
| — | — | 26 | 102.4 | 0.9898 | 2.6 | 3.247 |
| 10 | — | — | 101.9 | 0.9989 | 2.589 | 3.277 |
| — | — | 24 | 94.49 | 1.162 | 2.4 | 3.811 |
| — | 13 | — | 92 | 1.225 | 2.337 | 4.020 |
| 11 | — | — | 90.74 | 1.260 | 2.305 | 4.134 |
| — | — | 22 | 86.61 | 1.382 | 2.2 | 4.535 |
| 12 | — | — | 80.81 | 1.588 | 2.053 | 5.210 |
| — | 14 | — | 80 | 1.658 | 2.032 | 5.440 |
| — | — | 20 | 78.74 | 1.673 | 2.0 | 5.488 |
| — | 15 | — | 72 | 2.001 | 1.829 | 6.563 |
| 13 | — | — | 71.96 | 2.003 | 1.828 | 6.572 |
| — | — | 18 | 70.87 | 2.065 | 1.8 | 6.775 |
| 14 | — | — | 64.08 | 2.525 | 1.628 | 8.284 |
| — | 16 | — | 64 | 2.532 | 1.626 | 8.307 |
| — | — | 16 | 62.99 | 2.614 | 1.6 | 8.575 |
| 15 | — | — | 57.07 | 3.184 | 1.450 | 10.47 |
| — | 17 | — | 56 | 3.307 | 1.422 | 10.85 |
| — | — | 14 | 55.12 | 3.414 | 1.4 | 11.20 |
| 16 | — | — | 50.82 | 4.016 | 1.291 | 13.18 |
| — | 18 | — | 48 | 4.501 | 1.219 | 14.77 |
| — | — | 12 | 47.24 | 4.646 | 1.2 | 15.24 |
| 17 | — | — | 45.26 | 5.064 | 1.150 | 16.61 |
| — | — | 11 | 43.31 | 5.530 | 1.1 | 18.14 |
| 18 | — | — | 40.30 | 6.385 | 1.024 | 20.95 |
| — | 19 | — | 40 | 6.482 | 1.016 | 21.27 |

| GAUGE | | | ENGLISH UNITS | | METRIC UNITS | |
|---|---|---|---|---|---|---|
| B & S | S.W.G. | Metric | Diam. mils | Ohms per 1,000 ft | Diam. mm | Ohms per Km |
| — | — | 10 | 39.37 | 6.691 | 1.0 | 21.95 |
| — | 20 | — | 36 | 8.002 | 0.9144 | 26.25 |
| 19 | — | — | 35.89 | 8.051 | 0.9119 | 26.41 |
| — | — | 9 | 35.51 | 8.222 | 0.9 | 26.98 |
| — | 21 | — | 32 | 10.13 | 0.8128 | 33.23 |
| 20 | — | — | 31.96 | 10.15 | 0.8120 | 33.30 |
| — | — | 8 | 31.50 | 10.45 | 0.8 | 34.30 |
| 21 | — | — | 28.46 | 12.80 | 0.7231 | 41.99 |
| — | 22 | — | 28 | 13.23 | 0.7112 | 43.40 |
| — | — | 7 | 27.56 | 13.65 | 0.7 | 44.80 |
| 22 | — | — | 25.35 | 16.14 | 0.6440 | 52.95 |
| — | 23 | — | 24 | 18.00 | 0.6096 | 59.07 |
| — | — | 6 | 23.62 | 18.59 | 0.6 | 60.98 |
| 23 | — | — | 22.57 | 20.36 | 0.5734 | 66.80 |
| — | 24 | — | 22 | 21.43 | 0.5588 | 70.30 |
| — | — | 5.5 | 21.65 | 22.12 | 0.55 | 72.57 |
| 24 | — | — | 20.10 | 25.67 | 0.5107 | 84.22 |
| — | 25 | — | 20 | 25.93 | 0.5080 | 85.06 |
| — | — | 5 | 19.69 | 26.76 | 0.5 | 87.81 |
| — | 26 | — | 18 | 32.01 | 0.4572 | 105.0 |
| 25 | — | — | 17.90 | 32.37 | 0.4548 | 106.2 |
| — | — | 4.5 | 17.72 | 33.04 | 0.45 | 108.4 |
| — | 27 | — | 16.4 | 38.56 | 0.4162 | 126.5 |
| 26 | — | — | 15.94 | 40.81 | 0.4050 | 133.9 |
| — | — | 4 | 15.75 | 41.82 | 0.4 | 137.2 |
| — | 28 | — | 14.8 | 47.35 | 0.3759 | 155.3 |
| 27 | — | — | 14.20 | 51.47 | 0.3608 | 168.9 |
| — | — | 3.5 | 13.78 | 61.28 | 0.35 | 179.2 |
| — | 29 | — | 13.6 | 56.07 | 0.3454 | 184.0 |
| 28 | — | — | 12.64 | 64.90 | 0.3211 | 212.9 |
| — | 30 | — | 12.4 | 67.45 | 0.1350 | 221.3 |
| — | — | 3 | 11.81 | 74.34 | 0.3 | 243.9 |
| — | 31 | — | 11.6 | 77.07 | 0.2946 | 252.9 |
| 29 | — | — | 11.26 | 81.83 | 0.2861 | 268.5 |
| — | — | 2.8 | 11.02 | 85.34 | 0.28 | 280.0 |
| — | 32 | — | 10.8 | 88.91 | 0.2743 | 291.7 |
| — | — | 2.6 | 10.24 | 98.98 | 0.26 | 324.7 |
| 30 | — | — | 10.03 | 103.2 | 0.2548 | 338.6 |
| — | 33 | — | 10.0 | 103.7 | 0.2540 | 340.2 |
| — | — | 2.4 | 9.449 | 116.2 | 0.24 | 381.1 |
| — | 34 | — | 9.2 | 122.5 | 0.2337 | 402.0 |
| 31 | — | — | 8.928 | 130.1 | 0.2268 | 426.8 |

| GAUGE | | | ENGLISH UNITS | | METRIC UNITS | |
|---|---|---|---|---|---|---|
| B & S | S.W.G. | Metric | Diam. mils | Ohms per 1,000 ft | Diam mm | Ohms per Km |
| — | — | 2.2 | 8.661 | 138.2 | 0.22 | 453.5 |
| — | 35 | — | 8.4 | 147.0 | 0.2134 | 482.2 |
| 32 | — | — | 7.950 | 164.1 | 0.2020 | 538.4 |
| — | — | 2.0 | 7.874 | 167.3 | 0.2 | 548.8 |
| — | 36 | — | 7.6 | 179.5 | 0.1930 | 589.1 |
| — | — | 1.8 | 7.087 | 206.5 | 0.18 | 677.5 |
| 33 | — | — | 7.080 | 206.9 | 0.1799 | 678.8 |
| — | 37 | — | 6.8 | 224.3 | 0.1727 | 735.8 |
| 34 | — | — | 6.305 | 260.9 | 0.1602 | 856.0 |
| — | — | 1.6 | 6.299 | 261.4 | 0.16 | 857.5 |
| — | 38 | — | 6.0 | 288.1 | 0.1524 | 945.1 |
| 35 | — | — | 5.615 | 329.0 | 0.1427 | 1079 |
| — | — | 1.4 | 5.512 | 314.4 | 0.14 | 1120 |
| — | 39 | — | 5.2 | 383.5 | 0.1321 | 1258 |
| 36 | — | — | 5.000 | 414.8 | 0.1270 | 1361 |
| — | 40 | — | 4.8 | 450.1 | 0.1219 | 1477 |
| — | — | 1.2 | 4.724 | 464.6 | 0.12 | 1524 |
| 37 | — | — | 4.453 | 523.1 | 0.1131 | 1716 |
| — | 41 | — | 4.4 | 535.7 | 0.1118 | 1757 |
| — | — | 1.1 | 4.331 | 553.0 | 0.11 | 1814 |
| — | 42 | — | 4.0 | 648.2 | 0.1016 | 2127 |
| 38 | — | — | 3.965 | 659.6 | 0.1007 | 2164 |
| — | — | 1.0 | 3.937 | 669.1 | 0.1 | 2195 |
| — | 43 | — | 3.6 | 800.2 | .09144 | 2625 |
| — | — | 0.9 | 3.551 | 822.2 | .09 | 2698 |
| 39 | — | — | 3.531 | 831.8 | .08971 | 2729 |
| — | 44 | — | 3.2 | 1013 | .08128 | 3323 |
| — | — | 0.8 | 3.150 | 1045 | .08 | 3430 |
| 40 | — | — | 3.145 | 1049 | .07990 | 3442 |
| 41 | — | — | 2.801 | 1323 | .07115 | 4341 |
| — | 45 | — | 2.8 | 1323 | .07112 | 4340 |
| — | — | 0.7 | 2.756 | 1365 | .07 | 4480 |
| 42 | — | — | 2.494 | 1669 | .06336 | 5476 |
| — | 46 | — | 2.4 | 1800 | .06096 | 5907 |
| — | — | 0.6 | 2.362 | 1859 | .06 | 6098 |
| 43 | — | — | 2.221 | 2104 | .05643 | 6903 |
| — | — | 0.55 | 2.165 | 2212 | .055 | 7257 |
| — | 47 | — | 2.0 | 2593 | .05080 | 8506 |
| 44 | — | — | 1.978 | 2654 | .05025 | 8707 |
| — | — | 0.5 | 1.969 | 2676 | .05 | 8781 |

# Table 13.  Metric Copper Wire Tables

Column
(1)  Diameter of wire in mm
(2)  Area wire in square mm
(3)  Resistance ohms per 100 metres
(4)  Weight grams per metre length
(5)  Resistance in ohms 100 ft
(6)  Length metres per ohm resistance
(7)  Number turns close wound per square cm
(8)  Nearest SWG equivalent
(9)  Nearest AWG equivalent

| (1) | (2) | (3) | (4) | (5) | (6) | (7) | (8) | (9) |
|---|---|---|---|---|---|---|---|---|
| 0.03 | 0.000707 | 2350 | 6.29 | 716 | 0.0426 | 43000 | 49 | — |
| 0.04 | 0.00126 | 1320 | 11.2 | 402 | 0.0720 | 28200 | 48 | — |
| 0.05 | 0.00196 | 894 | 17.5 | 272 | 0.112 | 23500 | 47 | — |
| 0.06 | 0.00283 | 619 | 25.2 | 188 | 0.162 | 16200 | 46 | — |
| 0.07 | 0.00385 | 455 | 34.4 | 139 | 0.220 | 11900 | 45 | — |
| 0.08 | 0.00503 | 350 | 44.9 | 107 | 0.228 | 10700 | 44 | 40 |
| 0.09 | 0.00636 | 276 | 56.0 | 84 | 0.364 | 8600 | 43 | 39 |
| 0.10 | 0.00785 | 224 | 69.9 | 68 | 0.448 | 6700 | 42 | 38 |
| 0.12 | 0.0113 | 155 | 101 | 47 | 0.646 | 4860 | 40 | 37 |
| 0.15 | 0.0177 | 99 | 158 | 30 | 1.01 | 3120 | 38 | 35 |
| 0.16 | 0.0201 | 87 | 179 | 27 | 1.15 | 2760 | 38 | 34 |
| 0.18 | 0.0254 | 69 | 226 | 21 | 1.45 | 2270 | 37 | 33 |
| 0.20 | 0.0314 | 55.8 | 280 | 17 | 1.80 | 1890 | 36 | 32 |
| 0.22 | 0.0380 | 46.1 | 339 | 14 | 2.18 | 1540 | 35 | 31 |
| 0.25 | 0.0491 | 35.7 | 438 | 11 | 2.80 | 1230 | 33 | 30 |
| 0.27 | 0.0573 | 30.6 | 511 | 9.3 | 3.28 | 1060 | 32 | 29 |
| 0.28 | 0.0616 | 28.5 | 550 | 8.7 | 3.52 | 1000 | 32 | 29 |
| 0.30 | 0.0707 | 24.8 | 629 | 7.6 | 4.03 | 890 | 31 | 29 |
| 0.32 | 0.0804 | 21.8 | 716 | 6.6 | 4.60 | 750 | 30 | 28 |
| 0.35 | 0.0962 | 18.2 | 857 | 5.54 | 5.49 | 640 | 29 | 27 |
| 0.38 | 0.113 | 15.5 | 1010 | 4.72 | 6.47 | 560 | 28 | 27 |
| 0.40 | 0.124 | 13.96 | 1120 | 4.25 | 7.20 | 510 | 27 | 26 |
| 0.45 | 0.159 | 11.20 | 1420 | 3.41 | 9.09 | 400 | 26 | 25 |
| 0.50 | 0.196 | 8.90 | 1750 | 2.71 | 11.2 | 310 | 25 | 24 |
| 0.55 | 0.237 | 7.38 | 2110 | 2.25 | 13.5 | 270 | 24 | 23 |
| 0.60 | 0.283 | 6.21 | 2520 | 1.89 | 16.2 | 230 | 23 | 23 |
| 0.65 | 0.332 | 5.29 | 2960 | 1.61 | 19.0 | 199 | 23 | 22 |
| 0.70 | 0.385 | 4.56 | 3440 | 1.39 | 22.0 | 174 | 22 | 21 |
| 0.75 | 0.442 | 3.97 | 3930 | 1.21 | 25.2 | 132 | 22 | 21 |
| 0.80 | 0.503 | 3.49 | 4490 | 1.06 | 28.8 | 118 | 21 | 20 |
| 0.85 | 0.567 | 3.11 | 5070 | 0.95 | 32.5 | 106 | 21 | 20 |
| 0.90 | 0.636 | 2.76 | 5680 | 0.84 | 36.4 | 96 | 20 | 19 |
| 0.95 | 0.709 | 2.47 | 6310 | 0.75 | 40.5 | 87 | 20 | 19 |
| 1.00 | 0.785 | 2.26 | 6990 | 0.69 | 44.8 | — | 19 | 18 |
| 1.10 | 0.950 | 1.88 | 8470 | 0.57 | 51.4 | — | 19 | 17 |
| 1.20 | 1.131 | 1.58 | 10100 | 0.48 | 64.6 | — | 18 | 17 |
| 1.30 | 1.33 | 1.34 | 11900 | 0.41 | 76.2 | — | 18 | 16 |
| 1.40 | 1.54 | 1.16 | 13700 | 0.35 | 88.2 | — | 17 | 15 |
| 1.50 | 1.77 | 1.01 | 15800 | 0.31 | 101 | — | 16 | 15 |
| 1.60 | 2.01 | 0.887 | 17900 | 0.27 | 115 | — | 16 | 14 |
| 1.70 | 2.27 | 0.785 | 20200 | 0.24 | 130 | — | 15 | 14 |
| 1.80 | 2.54 | 0.700 | 22600 | 0.21 | 145 | — | 15 | 13 |
| 1.90 | 2.84 | 0.628 | 25300 | 0.19 | 163 | — | 15 | 13 |
| 2.00 | 3.14 | 0.567 | 28000 | 0.17 | 180 | — | 14 | 12 |
| 2.20 | 3.80 | 0.468 | 33900 | 0.14 | 218 | — | 13 | 11 |
| 2.50 | 4.91 | 0.363 | 43800 | 0.11 | 280 | — | 12 | 10 |
| 3.00 | 7.07 | 0.252 | 62900 | 0.08 | 405 | — | 11 | 9 |
| 3.50 | 9.62 | 0.185 | 85700 | 0.06 | 550 | — | 10 | 7 |
| 4.00 | 12.60 | 0.142 | 112000 | 0.04 | 720 | — | 8 | 6 |

## Table 14. U.S.A. Copper Wire Tables

Column
(1) Wire size AWG or B & S
(2) Diameter in mils = 1/1000 in
(3) Circular area in mils
(4) Turns per inch linear
(5) Feet per lb bare
(6) Ohms per 1000 ft

| (1) | (2) | (3) | (4) | (5) | (6) |
|---|---|---|---|---|---|
| 1 | 289.3 | 83690 | — | 3.947 | 0.1264 |
| 2 | 257.6 | 66370 | — | 4.977 | 0.1593 |
| 3 | 229.4 | 52640 | — | 6.276 | 0.2009 |
| 4 | 204.3 | 41740 | — | 7.914 | 0.2533 |
| 5 | 181.9 | 33100 | — | 9.980 | 0.3195 |
| 6 | 162.0 | 26250 | — | 12.58 | 0.4028 |
| 7 | 144.3 | 20820 | — | 15.87 | 0.5080 |
| 8 | 128.5 | 16510 | 7.6 | 20.01 | 0.6405 |
| 9 | 114.4 | 13090 | 8.6 | 25.23 | 0.8077 |
| 10 | 101.9 | 10380 | 9.6 | 31.82 | 1.018 |
| 11 | 90.7 | 8234 | 10.7 | 40.12 | 1.284 |
| 12 | 80.8 | 6530 | 12.0 | 50.59 | 1.619 |
| 13 | 72.0 | 5178 | 13.5 | 63.80 | 2.042 |
| 14 | 64.1 | 4107 | 15.0 | 80.44 | 2.575 |
| 15 | 57.1 | 3257 | 16.8 | 101.4 | 3.247 |
| 16 | 50.8 | 2583 | 18.9 | 127.9 | 4.094 |
| 17 | 45.3 | 2048 | 21.2 | 161.3 | 5.163 |
| 18 | 40.3 | 1624 | 23.6 | 203.4 | 6.510 |
| 19 | 35.9 | 1288 | 26.4 | 256.5 | 8.210 |
| 20 | 32.0 | 1022 | 29.4 | 323.4 | 10.35 |
| 21 | 28.5 | 810 | 33.1 | 407.8 | 13.05 |
| 22 | 25.3 | 642 | 37.0 | 514.2 | 16.46 |
| 23 | 22.6 | 510 | 41.3 | 648.4 | 20.76 |
| 24 | 20.1 | 404 | 46.3 | 817.7 | 26.17 |
| 25 | 17.9 | 320 | 51.7 | 1031 | 33.00 |
| 26 | 15.9 | 254 | 58.0 | 1300 | 41.62 |
| 27 | 14.2 | 202 | 64.9 | 1639 | 52.48 |
| 28 | 12.6 | 160 | 72.7 | 2067 | 66.17 |
| 29 | 11.3 | 127 | 81.6 | 2607 | 83.44 |
| 30 | 10.0 | 101 | 90.5 | 3287 | 105.2 |
| 31 | 8.9 | 80 | 101 | 4145 | 132.7 |
| 32 | 8.0 | 63 | 113 | 5227 | 167.3 |
| 33 | 7.1 | 50 | 127 | 6591 | 211.0 |
| 34 | 6.3 | 40 | 143 | 8310 | 266.0 |
| 35 | 5.6 | 32 | 158 | 10480 | 335 |
| 36 | 5.0 | 25 | 175 | 13210 | 423 |
| 37 | 4.5 | 20 | 198 | 16660 | 533 |
| 38 | 4.0 | 16 | 224 | 21010 | 673 |
| 39 | 3.5 | 12 | 248 | 26500 | 848 |
| 40 | 3.1 | 10 | 282 | 33410 | 1070 |

# Table 15. S.W.G. Details

| S. W. G. | Dia in inches | Area circular mils | Ohms per 1000 yds | Ohms per pound (lb) | Yards per pound (lb) | lbs per 1000 yards | Turns per inch close | | |
|---|---|---|---|---|---|---|---|---|---|
| | | | | | | | enamel | single silk | double silk |
| 7/0 | 0.500 | 250000 | 0.12227 | 0.000053 | 0.440 | 2271 | | | |
| 6/0 | 0.464 | 215296 | 0.14202 | 0.000073 | 0.511 | 1955 | | | |
| 5/0 | 0.432 | 186624 | 0.16379 | 0.000096 | 0.589 | 1695 | | | |
| 4/0 | 0.400 | 160000 | 0.19110 | 0.000132 | 0.688 | 1453 | | | |
| 3/0 | 0.372 | 138384 | 0.2209 | 0.000175 | 0.797 | 1257 | | | |
| 2/0 | 0.348 | 121104 | 0.2526 | 0.000229 | 0.910 | 1100 | | | |
| 1/0 | 0.324 | 104976 | 0.2912 | 0.000305 | 1.049 | 953 | | | |
| 1 | 0.300 | 105000 | 0.3396 | 0.000415 | 1.228 | 818 | | | |
| 2 | 0.276 | 76176 | 0.4013 | 0.000580 | 1.446 | 692 | | | |
| 3 | 0.252 | 63504 | 0.4815 | 0.000834 | 1.733 | 577 | | | |
| 4 | 0.232 | 53824 | 0.5679 | 0.001162 | 2.046 | 489 | | | |
| 5 | 0.212 | 44944 | 0.6804 | 0.001666 | 2.449 | 408 | | | |
| 6 | 0.192 | 36864 | 0.8292 | 0.002476 | 2.987 | 335 | | | |
| 7 | 0.176 | 30976 | 0.9870 | 0.003507 | 3.55 | 281 | | | |
| 8 | 0.160 | 25600 | 1.194 | 0.005135 | 4.30 | 232 | | | |
| 9 | 0.144 | 20736 | 1.474 | 0.007827 | 5.31 | 188 | | | |
| 10 | 0.128 | 16384 | 1.866 | 0.012537 | 6.72 | 149 | 7.8 | | |
| 11 | 0.116 | 13456 | 2.272 | 0.018587 | 8.18 | 122 | 8.3 | | |
| 12 | 0.104 | 10816 | 2.826 | 0.02877 | 10 | 98.2 | 9.3 | | |
| 13 | 0.092 | 8464 | 3.612 | 0.04698 | 13 | 76.9 | 10.4 | | |
| 14 | 0.080 | 6400 | 4.776 | 0.08216 | 17 | 58.1 | 11.9 | | |
| 15 | 0.072 | 5184 | 5.897 | 0.12520 | 21 | 47.1 | 13.2 | | |
| 16 | 0.064 | 4096 | 6.611 | 0.2006 | 27 | 37.2 | 14.8 | 14,9 | 14.7 |
| 17 | 0.056 | 3136 | 9.747 | 0.3422 | 35 | 28.5 | 16.9 | 16.9 | 16.6 |
| 18 | 0.048 | 2304 | 13.27 | 0.6340 | 48 | 20.9 | 19.7 | 20.0 | 19.6 |
| 19 | 0.04 | 1600 | 19.11 | 1.315 | 69 | 14.5 | 23.5 | 23.8 | 23.3 |
| 20 | 0.036 | 1296 | 23.59 | 2.004 | 85 | 11.8 | 26.0 | 26.3 | 25.7 |
| 21 | 0.032 | 1024 | 29.85 | 3.209 | 108 | 9.3 | 29.2 | 29.4 | 28.6 |
| 22 | 0.028 | 784 | 38.99 | 5.475 | 140 | 7.12 | 33.0 | 33.3 | 32.3 |
| 23 | 0.024 | 576 | 53.07 | 10.14 | 191 | 5.23 | 38.3 | 38.5 | 37.1 |
| 24 | 0.022 | 484 | 63.16 | 14.37 | 228 | 4.4 | 42.4 | 42.6 | 40.0 |
| 25 | 0.020 | 400 | 76.42 | 21.03 | 275 | 3.63 | 46.5 | 46.5 | 43.5 |
| 26 | 0.018 | 324 | 94.35 | 32.06 | 339 | 2.94 | 51.5 | 51.8 | 48.5 |
| 27 | 0.0164 | 268.96 | 113.6 | 46.52 | 410 | 2.44 | 56.5 | 56.5 | 52.9 |
| 28 | 0.0148 | 219.04 | 139.6 | 70.14 | 503 | 1.99 | 62.5 | 62.1 | 57.8 |
| 29 | 0.0136 | 184.96 | 165.3 | 98.37 | 595 | 1.68 | 67.6 | 67.1 | 62.1 |
| 30 | 0.0124 | 153.76 | 198.8 | 142.4 | 716 | 1.4 | 74.6 | 73.0 | 67.1 |
| 31 | 0.0116 | 134.56 | 227.2 | 185.9 | 818 | 1.22 | 79.4 | 77.5 | 70.9 |
| 32 | 0.0108 | 116.64 | 262.1 | 247.4 | 944 | 1.06 | 85.7 | 82.6 | 75.2 |
| 33 | 0.010 | 100.0 | 305.7 | 336.5 | 1101 | 0.908 | 91.7 | 88.5 | 80.1 |
| 34 | 0.0092 | 84.64 | 361.2 | 469.8 | 1300 | 0.769 | 100 | 95.2 | 85.5 |
| 35 | 0.0084 | 70.56 | 433.2 | 676.0 | 1564 | 0.641 | 109 | 103 | 92.0 |
| 36 | 0.0076 | 57.76 | 529.2 | 1009 | 1906 | 0.525 | 120 | 112 | 99.0 |
| 37 | 0.0068 | 46.24 | 661.1 | 1574 | 2381 | 0.420 | 135 | 123 | 107.0 |
| 38 | 0.0060 | 36.0 | 849.1 | 2596 | 3058 | 0.327 | 151 | 137 | 118.0 |
| 39 | 0.0052 | 27.04 | 1130 | 4603 | 4070 | 0.246 | 175 | 154 | 130.0 |
| 40 | 0.0048 | 23.04 | 1327 | 6340 | 4777 | 0.209 | 189 | 164 | 137.0 |
| 41 | 0.0044 | 19.36 | 1579 | 8979 | 5687 | 0.176 | 208 | 179 | 151.0 |
| 42 | 0.004 | 16.0 | 1911 | 13146 | 6880 | 0.145 | 227 | 192 | 161.0 |
| 43 | 0.0036 | 12.96 | 2359 | 20040 | 8493 | 0.118 | 256 | 208 | 172.0 |
| 44 | 0.0032 | 10.24 | 2985 | 32090 | 10753 | 0.093 | 285 | 227 | 185.0 |
| 45 | 0.0028 | 7.84 | 3899 | 54750 | 14040 | 0.071 | 322 | 250 | 200.0 |
| 46 | 0.0024 | 5.76 | 5307 | 101400 | 19113 | 0.052 | 377 | 278 | 217.0 |
| 47 | 0.002 | 4.00 | 7642 | 210300 | 27527 | 0.036 | 444 | 312 | 238.0 |
| 48 | 0.0016 | 2.56 | 11941 | 513500 | 43000 | 0.023 | | | |
| 49 | 0.0012 | 1.44 | 21230 | 1623000 | 76466 | 0.013 | | | |
| 50 | 0.001 | 1.00 | 30570 | 3365000 | 101000 | 0.009 | | | |

| wound single cotton | double cotton | Turns per square inch | | | | | Current at 1000 amps per sq inch | Sectional area of wire in sq inches | Length per ohms of wire in yds |
|---|---|---|---|---|---|---|---|---|---|
| | | enamel | single silk | double silk | single cotton | double cotton | | | |
| | | | | | | | 196 | 0.1963 | 8179 |
| | | | | | | | 169 | 0.1691 | 7042 |
| | | | | | | | 147 | 0.1466 | 6105 |
| | | | | | | | 126 | 0.1257 | 5233 |
| | | | | | | | 109 | 0.1090 | 4531 |
| | | | | | | | 95.1 | 0.0951 | 3961 |
| | | | | | | | 82.5 | 0.0825 | 3434 |
| | | | | | | | 70.7 | 0.0707 | 2945 |
| | | | | | | | 59.9 | 0.0598 | 2491 |
| | | | | | | | 49.9 | 0.0499 | 2077 |
| | | | | | | | 42.3 | 0.0423 | 1761 |
| | | | | | | | 35.3 | 0.0353 | 1469 |
| | | | | | | | 28.9 | 0.0289 | 1206 |
| | | | | | | | 24.3 | 0.0243 | 1013 |
| | | | | | | | 20.1 | 0.0201 | 837 |
| | | | | | | | 16.3 | 0.0163 | 678 |
| 7.3 | 7.1 | 58 | | | | 49 | 12.9 | 0.0129 | 536 |
| 8.1 | 7.7 | 69 | | | | 59 | 10.6 | 0.0106 | 440.1 |
| 8.9 | 8.5 | 86 | | | | 72 | 8.50 | 0.00849 | 354.1 |
| 10.0 | 9.4 | 108 | | | | 89 | 6.65 | 0.00665 | 276.9 |
| 11.4 | 10.6 | 141 | | | | 113 | 5.03 | 0.00503 | 209.9 |
| 12.7 | 11.9 | 175 | | | | 141 | 4.07 | 0.00467 | 169.9 |
| 14.1 | 13.2 | 219 | 216 | 210 | 193 | 169 | 3.22 | 0.00322 | 151.3 |
| 15.9 | 14.7 | 285 | 279 | 272 | 246 | 216 | 2.46 | 0.00246 | 102.6 |
| 18.2 | 16.9 | 388 | 392 | 376 | 324 | 285 | 1.81 | 0.00181 | 75.36 |
| 21.3 | 19.6 | 550 | 552 | 529 | 441 | 384 | 1.26 | 0.00126 | 52.33 |
| 23.8 | 21.3 | 676 | 676 | 640 | 552 | 451 | 1.02 | 0.00102 | 42.37 |
| 26.3 | 23.3 | 852 | 847 | 800 | 681 | 540 | 0.804 | 0.00080 | 33.51 |
| 29.4 | 25.6 | 1089 | 1089 | 1017 | 846 | 655 | 0.616 | 0.00062 | 25.64 |
| 34.5 | 29.4 | 1513 | 1568 | 1350 | 1169 | 860 | 0.452 | 0.00045 | 18.85 |
| 37.1 | 31.2 | 1789 | 1800 | 1590 | 1346 | 971 | 0.380 | 0.00038 | 15.84 |
| 40.0 | 33.3 | 2070 | 2160 | 1860 | 1568 | 1105 | 0.314 | 0.00031 | 13.09 |
| 43.5 | 35.7 | 2650 | 2600 | 2300 | 1850 | 1270 | 0.255 | 0.00025 | 10.608 |
| 46.7 | 37.9 | 3190 | 3170 | 2750 | 2100 | 1430 | 0.211 | 0.00021 | 8.803 |
| 50.5 | 40.3 | 3900 | 3800 | 3300 | 2500 | 1620 | 0.172 | 0.00017 | 7.163 |
| 53.8 | 42.4 | 4550 | 4450 | 3800 | 2800 | 1790 | 0.145 | 0.00014 | 6.050 |
| 57.5 | 44.6 | 5550 | 5300 | 4450 | 3250 | 1980 | 0.121 | 0.00012 | 5.030 |
| 60.3 | 46.3 | 6300 | 6000 | 5000 | 3550 | 2140 | 0.106 | 0.00011 | 4.405 |
| 63.3 | 48.1 | 7300 | 6800 | 5600 | 3950 | 2340 | 0.092 | 0.000092 | 3.817 |
| 66.7 | 50.1 | 8400 | 7800 | 6400 | 4350 | 2500 | 0.078 | 0.000078 | 3.271 |
| 70.4 | 52.1 | 10000 | 9000 | 7300 | 4850 | 2700 | 0.066 | 0.000066 | 2.770 |
| 80.6 | 57.5 | 12000 | 10000 | 8400 | 6400 | 3300 | 0.055 | 0.000055 | 2.309 |
| 86.2 | 60.2 | 14500 | 12500 | 9750 | 7370 | 3600 | 0.045 | 0.000045 | 1.890 |
| 99.2 | 63.3 | 18200 | 15000 | 11000 | 9650 | 4000 | 0.036 | 0.000036 | 1.513 |
| 100.0 | 66.7 | 22900 | 18500 | 13500 | 9900 | 4400 | 0.028 | 0.000028 | 1.178 |
| 109.0 | 70.4 | 30600 | 23500 | 16500 | 11500 | 4900 | 0.021 | 0.000021 | 0.885 |
| 114.0 | 72.5 | 35600 | 26500 | 18500 | 12600 | 5200 | 0.018 | 0.000018 | 0.750 |
| | | 43000 | 32000 | 22000 | | | 0.015 | 0.000015 | 0.633 |
| | | 51000 | 36500 | 25500 | | | 0.012 | 0.000012 | 0.520 |
| | | 65000 | 43000 | 29000 | | | 0.010 | 0.00001 | 0.424 |
| | | 81000 | 51200 | 34000 | | | 0.008 | | 0.336 |
| | | 104000 | 62000 | 39500 | | | 0.0061 | | 0.256 |
| | | 142000 | 72000 | 46500 | | | 0.0045 | | 0.188 |
| | | 197000 | 97000 | 56000 | | | 0.0031 | | 0.131 |
| | | | | | | | 0.0021 | | 0.048 |
| | | | | | | | 0.0011 | | 0.047 |
| | | | | | | | 0.0007 | | 0.033 |

# Table 16. Resistance Wire Details

| S.W.G. | Nickel silver wire Resistance ohms per 1000 ft approx. | Resistance ohms per ounce approx. | Amperage reqd. for temperature rise of 200°C | 100°C | Manganin wire Resistance ohms per 1000 ft approx. | ohms per ounce approx. | Amperage reqd. for temperature rise of 200°C | 100°C | Planinoid wire Resistance ohms per 1000 ft approx. | ohms per ounce approx. | Amperage reqd. for temperature rise of 200°C | 100°C | Dia. in inches |
|---|---|---|---|---|---|---|---|---|---|---|---|---|---|
| 8 | — | — | — | — | 9.6 | 0.008 | 61 | 39 | 9.5 | 0.008 | — | — | 0.160 |
| 10 | — | — | — | — | 15.0 | 0.018 | 39 | 27 | 14.9 | 0.018 | — | — | 0.180 |
| 12 | — | — | — | — | 22.7 | 0.042 | 28 | 21 | 22.7 | 0.042 | — | — | 0.104 |
| 14 | — | — | — | 8.1 | 38.3 | 0.12 | 17.5 | 11.7 | 38.4 | 0.12 | — | — | 0.080 |
| 16 | 34 | 0.17 | 14.2 | 6.1 | 59.6 | 0.30 | 10.1 | 7.2 | 59.7 | 0.31 | — | — | 0.064 |
| 18 | 59 | 0.53 | 9.4 | 4.1 | 107 | 0.95 | 7.6 | 5.1 | 108 | 0.95 | — | — | 0.048 |
| 20 | 109 | 1.7 | 6.3 | — | 190 | 2.9 | 5.1 | 3.6 | 189 | 2.9 | — | — | 0.036 |
| 21 | — | — | — | — | 241 | 4.9 | — | — | — | — | — | — | 0.032 |
| 22 | 180 | 5.04 | 4.2 | 3.1 | 315 | 8.8 | 3.8 | 2.6 | 316 | 8.7 | — | — | 0.028 |
| 23 | — | — | — | — | 428 | 15 | — | — | — | — | — | — | 0.024 |
| 24 | 292 | 12.25 | — | — | 510 | 21 | — | — | 509 | 22 | — | — | 0.022 |
| 25 | — | — | — | — | 617 | 32 | — | — | — | — | — | — | 0.020 |
| 26 | 437 | 27.56 | — | — | 763 | 48 | — | — | 764 | 48 | — | — | 0.018 |
| 27 | — | — | — | — | 918 | 70 | — | — | — | — | — | — | 0.0164 |
| 28 | 669 | 64.37 | — | — | 1166 | 112 | — | — | 1165 | 112 | — | — | 0.0148 |
| 30 | 917 | 121 | — | — | 1600 | 211 | — | — | 1601 | 212 | — | — | 0.0124 |
| 32 | — | — | — | — | 2105 | 367 | — | — | 2104 | 367 | — | — | 0.0108 |
| 34 | — | — | — | — | 2935 | 704 | — | — | 2933 | 705 | — | — | 0.0092 |
| 36 | — | — | — | — | 4303 | 1520 | — | — | 4305 | 1520 | — | — | 0.0076 |
| 38 | — | — | — | — | 6918 | 3900 | — | — | 6917 | 3901 | — | — | 0.006 |
| 40 | — | — | — | — | 10762 | 9530 | — | — | 10764 | 9531 | — | — | 0.0048 |
| 42 | — | — | — | — | 15413 | 19500 | — | — | 15416 | 19500 | — | — | 0.004 |
| 44 | — | — | — | — | 24083 | 48000 | — | — | 24087 | 48000 | — | — | 0.0032 |
| 46 | — | — | — | — | 42816 | 152000 | — | — | 48819 | 152000 | — | — | 0.0024 |

| 160 | Coil Design and Construction Manual | £2.50 |
|---|---|---|
| 227 | Beginners Guide to Building Electronic Projects | £1.95 |
| BP28 | Resistor Selection Handbook | £0.60 |
| BP36 | 50 Circuits Using Germanium Silicon & Zener Diodes | £1.95 |
| BP37 | 50 Projects Using Relays, SCRs and TRIACs | £2.95 |
| BP39 | 50 (FET) Field Effect Transistor Projects | £2.95 |
| BP42 | 50 Simple LED Circuits | £1.95 |
| BP44 | IC 555 Projects | £2.95 |
| BP48 | Electronic Projects for Beginners | £1.95 |
| BP49 | Popular Electronic Projects | £2.50 |
| BP53 | Practical Electronics Calculations & Formulae | £3.95 |
| BP56 | Electronic Security Devices | £2.95 |
| BP74 | Electronic Music Projects | £2.95 |
| BP76 | Power Supply Projects | £2.50 |
| BP78 | Practical Computer Experiments | £1.75 |
| BP80 | Popular Electronic Circuits – Book 1 | £2.95 |
| BP84 | Digital IC Projects | £1.95 |
| BP85 | International Transistor Equivalents Guide | £3.95 |
| BP87 | 50 Simple LED Circuits – Book 2 | £1.95 |
| BP88 | How to Use Op-amps | £2.95 |
| BP90 | Audio Projects | £2.50 |
| BP92 | Electronics Simplified – Crystal Set Construction | £1.75 |
| BP94 | Electronic Projects for Cars and Boats | £1.95 |
| BP95 | Model Railway Projects | £2.95 |
| BP97 | IC Projects for Beginners | £1.95 |
| BP98 | Popular Electronic Circuits – Book 2 | £2.95 |
| BP99 | Mini-matrix Board Projects | £2.50 |
| BP105 | Aerial Projects | £2.50 |
| BP107 | 30 Solderless Breadboard Projects – Book 1 | £2.95 |
| BP110 | How to Get Your Electronic Projects Working | £2.95 |
| BP111 | Audio | £3.95 |
| BP115 | The Pre-computer Book | £1.95 |
| BP118 | Practical Electronic Building Blocks – Book 2 | £1.95 |
| BP121 | How to Design and Make Your Own PCB's | £2.50 |
| BP122 | Audio Amplifier Construction | £2.95 |
| BP125 | 25 Simple Amateur Band Aerials | £1.95 |
| BP126 | BASIC & PASCAL in Parallel | £1.50 |
| BP130 | Micro Interfacing Circuits – Book 1 | £2.75 |
| BP131 | Micro Interfacing Circuits – Book 2 | £2.75 |
| BP132 | 25 Simple SW Broadcast Band Aerials | £1.95 |
| BP136 | 25 Simple Indoor and Window Aerials | £1.75 |
| BP137 | BASIC & FORTRAN in Parallel | £1.95 |
| BP138 | BASIC & FORTH in Parallel | £1.95 |
| BP144 | Further Practical Electronics Calculations & Formulae | £4.95 |
| BP145 | 25 Simple Tropical and MW Band Aerials | £1.75 |
| BP146 | The Pre-BASIC Book | £2.95 |
| BP147 | An Introduction to 6502 Machine Code | £2.95 |
| BP148 | Computer Terminology Explained | £1.95 |
| BP171 | Easy Add-on Projects for Amstrad CPC 464, 664, 6128 & MSX Computers | £2.95 |
| BP176 | A TV-DXers Handbook (Revised Edition) | £5.95 |
| BP177 | An Introduction to Computer Communications | £2.95 |
| BP179 | Electronic Circuits for the Computer Control of Robots | £2.95 |
| BP182 | MIDI Projects | £2.95 |
| BP184 | An Introduction to 68000 Assembly Language | £2.95 |
| BP187 | A Practical Reference Guide to Word Processing on the Amstrad PCW8256 & PCW8512 | £5.95 |
| BP190 | More Advanced Electronic Security Projects | £2.95 |
| BP192 | More Advanced Power Supply Projects | £2.95 |
| BP193 | LOGO for Beginners | £2.95 |
| BP196 | BASIC & LOGO in Parallel | £2.95 |
| BP197 | An Introduction to the Amstrad PC's | £5.95 |
| BP198 | An Introduction to Antenna Theory | £2.95 |
| BP230 | A Concise Introduction to GEM | £2.95 |
| BP232 | A Concise Introduction to MS-DOS | £2.95 |
| BP233 | Electronic Hobbyists Handbook | £4.95 |
| BP239 | Getting the Most From Your Multimeter | £2.95 |
| BP240 | Remote Control Handbook | £3.95 |
| BP243 | BBC BASIC86 on the Amstrad PC's & IBM Compatibles – Book 1: Language | £3.95 |
| BP244 | BBC BASIC86 on the Amstrad PC's & IBM Compatibles – Book 2: Graphics and Disk Files | £3.95 |
| BP245 | Digital Audio Projects | £2.95 |
| BP246 | Musical Applications of the Atari ST's | £5.95 |
| BP247 | More Advanced MIDI Projects | £2.95 |
| BP248 | Test Equipment Construction | £2.95 |
| BP249 | More Advanced Test Equipment Construction | £3.50 |
| BP250 | Programming in FORTRAN 77 | £4.95 |
| BP251 | Computer Hobbyists Handbook | £5.95 |
| BP254 | From Atoms to Amperes | £3.50 |
| BP255 | International Radio Stations Guide (Revised 1991/92 Edition) | £5.95 |
| BP256 | An Introduction to Loudspeakers & Enclosure Design | £2.95 |
| BP257 | An Introduction to Amateur Radio | £3.50 |
| BP258 | Learning to Program in C (Revised Edition) | £4.95 |
| BP259 | A Concise Introduction to UNIX | £2.95 |
| BP260 | A Concise Introduction to OS/2 | £2.95 |
| BP261 | A Concise Introduction to Lotus 1-2-3 (Revised Edition) | £3.95 |

| | | |
|---|---|---|
| BP262 | A Concise Introduction to Wordperfect (Revised Edition) | £3.95 |
| BP264 | A Concise Advanced User's Guide to MS-DOS (Revised Edition) | £3.95 |
| BP265 | More Advanced Uses of the Multimeter | £2.95 |
| BP266 | Electronic Modules and Systems for Beginners | £3.95 |
| BP267 | How to Use Oscilloscopes & Other Test Equipment | £3.50 |
| BP269 | An Introduction to Desktop Publishing | £5.95 |
| BP270 | A Concise Introduction to Symphony | £3.95 |
| BP271 | How to Expand, Modernise & Repair PC's & Compatibles | £3.95 |
| BP272 | Interfacing PC's and Compatibles | £3.95 |
| BP273 | Practical Electronic Sensors | £4.95 |
| BP274 | A Concise Introduction to SuperCalc5 | £3.95 |
| BP275 | Simple Short Wave Receiver Construction | £3.95 |
| BP276 | Short Wave Superhet Receiver Construction | £2.95 |
| BP277 | High Power Audio Amplifier Construction | £3.95 |
| BP278 | Experimental Antenna Topics | £3.50 |
| BP279 | A Concise Introduction to Excel | £3.95 |
| BP280 | Getting the Most From Your PC's Hard Disk | £3.95 |
| BP281 | An Introduction to VHF/UHF for Radio Amateurs | £3.50 |
| BP282 | Understanding PC Specifications | £3.95 |
| BP283 | A Concise Introduction to SmartWare II | £4.95 |
| BP284 | Programming in QuickBASIC | £4.95 |
| BP285 | A Beginners Guide to Modern Electronic Components | £3.95 |
| BP286 | A Reference Guide to Basic Electronics Terms | £5.95 |
| BP287 | A Reference Guide to Practical Electronics Terms | £5.95 |
| BP288 | A Concise Introduction to Windows3.0 | £3.95 |
| BP290 | An Introduction to Amateur Communications Satellite | £3.95 |
| BP291 | A Concise Introduction to Ventura | £3.95 |
| BP292 | Public Address Loudspeaker Systems | £3.95 |
| BP293 | An Introduction to Radio Wave Propagation | £3.95 |
| BP294 | A Concise Introduction to Microsoft Works | £4.95 |
| BP295 | A Concise Introduction to Word for Windows | £4.95 |
| BP297 | Loudspeakers for Musicians | £3.95 |
| BP298 | A Concise Introduction to the Mac System & Finder | £3.95 |
| BP299 | Practical Electronic Filters | £4.95 |
| BP300 | Setting Up An Amateur Radio Station | £3.95 |
| BP301 | Antennas for VHF and UHF | £3.95 |
| BP302 | A Concise Users Guide to Lotus 1-2-3 Release 3.1 | £3.95 |
| BP303 | Understanding PC Software | £4.95 |
| BP304 | Projects for Radio Amateurs and SWLs | £3.95 |
| BP305 | Learning CAD with AutoSketch for Windows | £5.95 |
| BP306 | A Concise Introduction to Ami Pro 3 | £4.95 |
| BP307 | A Concise Introduction to QuarkXPress | £4.95 |
| BP308 | A Concise Introduction to Word 5.1 on the Macintosh | £5.95 |
| BP309 | Preamplifier and Filter Circuits | £3.95 |
| BP310 | Acoustic Feedback – How to Avoid It | £3.95 |
| BP311 | An Introduction to Scanners and Scanning | £4.95 |
| BP312 | An Introduction to Microwaves | £3.95 |
| BP313 | A Concise Introduction to Sage | £3.95 |
| BP314 | A Concise Introduction to Quattro Pro | £4.95 |
| BP315 | An Introduction to the Electromagnetic Wave | £4.95 |
| BP316 | Practical Electronic Design Data | £4.95 |
| BP317 | Practical Electronic Timing | £4.95 |
| BP318 | A Concise User's Guide to MS-DOS 5 | £4.95 |
| BP319 | Making MS-DOS Work for You | £4.95 |
| BP320 | Electronic Projects for Your PC | £3.95 |
| BP321 | Circuit Source – Book 1 | £4.95 |
| BP322 | Circuit Source – Book 2 | £4.95 |
| BP323 | How to Choose a Small Business Computer System | £4.95 |
| BP324 | The Art of Soldering | £3.95 |
| BP325 | A Concise Users Guide to Windows3.1 | £4.95 |
| BP326 | The Electronics of Satellite Communications | £4.95 |
| BP327 | MS-DOS One Step at a Time | £4.95 |
| BP328 | Sage Explained | £5.95 |
| BP329 | Electronic Music Learning Projects | £4.95 |
| BP330 | A Concise User's Guide to Lotus 1-2-3 Release 2.4 | £4.95 |
| BP331 | A Beginners Guide to MIDI | £4.95 |
| BP332 | A Beginners Guide to TTL Digital ICs | £4.95 |
| BP333 | A Beginners Guide to CMOS Digital ICs | £4.95 |
| BP334 | Magic Electronic Projects | £4.95 |
| BP335 | Operational Amplifier User's Handbook | £5.95 |
| BP336 | A Concise User's Guide to Lotus 1-2-3 Release 3.4 | £5.95 |
| BP337 | A Concise Users Guide to Lotus 1-2-3 for Windows | £5.95 |
| BP338 | A Concise Introduction to Word for Windows | £5.95 |
| BP339 | A Concise Introduction to Wordperfect 5.2 for Windows | £5.95 |
| BP340 | A Concise Introduction to dBase V | £4.95 |
| BP341 | A Concise Users Guide to MS-DOS 6 | £5.95 |
| BP342 | A Conciser Users Guide to Lotus Improv | £5.95 |